A Vet Called Nigel

Nigel Taylor, BVetMed, DipVetMed (Guelph), MRCVS, always wanted to be a veterinary surgeon. Soon after he qualified from the Royal Veterinary College, London, he travelled to Canada to study and teach at a major Canadian veterinary school.

Today he runs his own busy veterinary practice in Plymouth, Devon, and appears regularly on BBC television's *Going Live!*, BBC Radio Devon and other radio and television programmes. He has a special interest in Veterinary Radiography and a lifelong enthusiasm for the Great Western Railway and Rough Collies.

D0766858

NIGEL TAYLOR

A Vet Called Nigel

Mandarin

A Mandarin Paperback
A VET CALLED NIGEL

First published in Great Britain 1992
by Mandarin Paperbacks
Michelin House, 81 Fulham Road, London SW3 6RB

Mandarin is an imprint of Reed Consumer Books Ltd

Copyright © Nigel Taylor 1992
The author has asserted his moral rights

A CIP catalogue record for this title
is available from the British Library

ISBN 0 7493 1225 4

Printed and bound in Great Britain
by Cox & Wyman Ltd, Reading

To Alf Wight MRCVS

'I tell you this, James.
There are great days ahead.'

Siegfried Farnon MRCVS

There are six veterinary schools in the United Kingdom. Every year many thousands apply to become veterinary surgeons.
Only a few hundred succeed.
And once, much to everyone's surprise, one of them was me. This is my story.
Most of it is true.

1

Cornwall exploded at dawn.

Not that the cow on the sofa was very impressed. Mind you, I couldn't blame her. There she was one moment enjoying the kind of spring morning the far west of Cornwall is famous for; the next she's plunging over the cliffside, heading at high speed for the beach below. A kamikaze with horns. The cause, a black and white collie, had long since disappeared: one short, sharp bark had been enough to startle the flummoxed Friesian and send her on her seaward plunge. For a moment there seemed to be nothing between her and a future as instant beefburger. Nothing, that is, except a cottage. Brian Chant's cottage.

'There's a cow in my upstairs bedroom,' Brian's voice bellowed down the phone.

'Of course,' I replied, trying to sound enthusiastic. Not easy at six in the morning when you've been up half the night playing midwife to a South Devon cow who should have gone on a diet long before she considered getting pregnant. 'How did she get there?'

'Through the roof. With a bloody great bang. About ten minutes ago.'

'What's she doing now?'

'She's on our sofa, watching breakfast TV. You'd better come quick.'

As I drove out of Helston taking the Lizard road I soon realised that I wasn't the only one heading for Brian Chant's cottage. First one, then a second fire engine hurtled by, sirens blaring, to be followed a moment later by two police Panda cars and an ambulance, lights flashing, skidding all over the road as they raced out towards the coast. The Great Porthallow Cow Rescue had begun.

My boss, John, was the expert when it came to rescuing cows from the Cornish coast. Usually it involved him flying to the rescue with one of the giant Sea King helicopters from RNAS Culdrose. Hovering like a hero above the waves he'd be winched down with a crewman and the cow would be plucked from the beach or the sea in a huge net which dangled like a giant conker from under the helicopter's belly.

'Nothing to it. Piece of cake,' he'd said, describing his most recent exploit, a bit like a Battle of Britain pilot describing a sortie. In fact I was sure that given half the chance silhouettes of rescued cows would be painted on his car wing to show the world what an ace he was. As he said himself, he was always being scrambled.

I'd never been scrambled before, but as I drove past Culdrose and watched a heavy Sea King lumber into the air I thought, this is it. A helicopter ride at last! By the time I arrived in Porthallow the rescue services were hard at work. Brian Chant's cottage was swarming with police. Up on the cliffside I could see firemen busy with ropes and winches. And above us all hovered a bright yellow helicopter making ready to send a crewman down over the side.

The fire chief said desperately, 'We can't move her. We've tried attaching ropes but every time we pull she struggles so much we can't budge her. You'll have to anaesthetise her if we're going to have any chance at all of getting her out.'

I followed him to Brian's cottage and pushing our way past the police on the stairs we made our way to the upstairs bedroom. Cornish cottages aren't made for crowds. The two-year-old Friesian was lying Cleopatra-like on an old, now very crumpled, sofa. Above her there was, just like in the cartoons, a cow-shaped hole in the roof. You could clearly see the outline of her head, legs and tail where she'd plummeted earthwards through the shingle. You could also see if you looked through the hole most of the St Keverne fire brigade who were strung up along the cliff's edge tugging at the reluctant cow like a vertical tug of war team.

Now, anaesthetising cows isn't as easy as you might think. They have got four stomachs, the biggest one of which is called the rumen. The rumen holds somewhere around sixty gallons of fluid and methane gas. That's why they belch a lot and why for all practical purposes the average cow is nothing more or less than a giant home brew kit on legs. If you give a cow a general anaesthetic, the chances are that it'll drown in all this fluid, so most cow surgery is done with the animal standing up under local anaesthesia.

Giving a cow a local can be a bit of a game too. Your patient soon lets you know, usually with its left foot, what it thinks of your technique. This either improves or you resign yourself to spending your whole life in country practice talking an octave higher.

'I can't anaesthetise her,' I explained. 'I might kill her. I'll give her a sedative instead.'

Cows are very sensitive to sedatives. You have to give quite a large dose to calm a horse but cows are such suckers you could almost just show them a bottle and they'd keel over. I injected a small dose of Xylazine into her tail vein and she started to snore contentedly.

'You can move her now,' I said confidently, as if treating cows in upstairs bedrooms was an everyday occurrence in veterinary practice.

I have to admit, the St Keverne Fire Brigade worked hard. A few 'all together lads', and the cow, still attached to her sofa, rose a good two feet into the air. And stayed there. There was no way they were going to be able to lift her back out through the hole in the roof. I could see the helicopter clattering away noisily as it hovered over the cliffside but the cottage was too close to the cliff's edge for the winchman to be lowered safely. There was only one thing for it.

'We'll take out the floor and lower her downstairs,' the fire chief announced with quiet desperation.

Suddenly I was surrounded by firemen hacking away at the floorboards with their axes. Pieces of wood and masonry were flying around everywhere. I must have looked anxious.

'Give him a helmet, Sid,' the chief barked. Sid, maybe a good foot taller and wider than me, thrust his yellow helmet onto my head where it balanced precariously. It was so large it felt like wearing a swimming pool.

'That'll keep you safe.'

Sid's helmet kept me safe all right. Before long only a couple of floorboards supported me and the cow, and I tiptoed along them like a trapeze artist scared of heights. The cow was past caring and snored loudly as they gently lowered her to the floor below still snuggled comfortably on her sofa. As the last floorboards finally gave way I jumped quickly down beside her.

The rescue was nearly over. She was starting to come out of her sedation and was getting restless. Sid and I levered the sofa off her. It had done its job, cushioning her fall and saving her from serious injury. In fact she was remarkably unscathed and before long was tottering towards the open door of the cottage.

By now there was quite a crowd outside in the village square all eagerly waiting for a glimpse of Brian Chant's unwelcome visitor. Someone found a halter and the fire chief led her to the open door. Sid and I pushed her steadily from behind and soon she and the chief were the centre of attention. Someone had called the press and Sid and I were ignored as the white-helmeted chief gave an interview to the *Falmouth Packet*. Suddenly a great cheer went up from the cliffside. The cow had caught sight of the hovering helicopter and didn't like it one bit. She was off and the chief, stopped in mid-sentence, was off with her.

He coped quite well with her gentle trot to begin with, but when she broke into a gallop he was done for. His pride stopped him from letting go of the halter and he was dragged first into a wild stumble and then a magnificent somersault. The St Keverne Fire Brigade were delighted and jumped and shouted on the cliffside with a wild whoop. Sid had the biggest grin I'd ever seen.

The reporter from the *Falmouth Packet* came over to us. He had a great story. Sort of thing that makes the *Sun*. He could see it now: 'Bouncing Bovine Bashes Building'. He seemed puzzled as he looked at me.

'Who the hell are you, mate, some sort of apprentice fireman?'

I was wearing a brown stock coat, fisherman's waders which protected my knees a lot better than wellingtons on the damp and muddy Cornish farms and, above it all, wobbling like mad, a giant yellow helmet. The syringe and needle in my right hand was a bit of a clue.

'Oh no,' said Sid, flashing me another grin, 'he's a real professional. Can't you see he's a bloody veterinary surgeon!'

2

I was dying. The trouble was, I wasn't very good at it. The consultant didn't sound very optimistic. 'Of course, the problem with these veterinary students is you can never be sure where they've been. You can catch some unpleasant diseases from animals, you know.'

He wasn't kidding. I was in an isolation hospital, where they took you when your illness was every bit as big a risk to everyone else as to you. A week before, someone had died of Green Monkey disease just a few rooms away. Somewhere along my corridor was a fourth-year veterinary student just back from Africa who'd fallen foul of malaria. And then there was me. Four days at the Royal Veterinary College and I was on my way out. Not the best of starts.

I've always wanted to be an animal doctor. No, tell a lie, there were a few years when I wanted to be a Beatle. I still do. I used to practise really hard. I knew all their songs by heart and I can still play the best left-handed air guitar in town. But Paul McCartney never rang so I set my heart on becoming a veterinary surgeon instead.

This isn't easy.

Mr Barkell, my careers master, tried to sound enthusiastic. With all the skill of someone who had spent years dealing with spotty youths like me who fancied a go at the veterinary world, he summed up my chances expertly, succinctly and to the point.

'You haven't got a hope.'

He smiled sympathetically, much like my bank manager does these days when we discuss happy matters like overdrafts, and then continued.

'You see, Taylor, you need to do very well in the sciences and to be honest, physics, chemistry and biology are not your strongest subjects. You are not a natural scientist.'

He had a point. Physics was a mystery to me. Endless experiments aimed at discovering something new about Archimedes' bathtime habits. Hundreds of formulae and calculations none of which I understood then, none of which I understand now. I would have killed for an electronic calculator if they'd been invented. As it was I found myself adrift in a sea of slide rules and logarithms. *Ugh*! Chemistry wasn't much better. Week after week we titrated the green solution into the blue solution until it turned red. The only excitement came when you got the mixture slightly wrong. Then with a few mysterious gurglings the blue solution turned yellow and exploded. No, Marie Curie could rest in peace, Devonport High was not going to make me the world's greatest chemist.

Somehow the biology master didn't seem to appreciate how much I wanted to work with animals. To him anything other than a plant was a creative afterthought. For a long time we ignored anything that Prince Charles couldn't have had a conversation with and spent long dreary afternoons dissecting dandelions and daisies; there are things about the natural world that grab me but xylem, cambium and phloem are not three of them. Our instructor only came to life when he told us of his travels in the South China Seas between the wars. These tales were mostly reserved for afternoon lessons and it didn't take us long to realise that the furthest east he ever travelled was to the Edgecumbe Arms at lunchtime, armed with the latest copy of the *National Geographic*. Still, anything was better than mosses and lichens and we would keep up the oriental pretence by asking him mind-expanding questions, not about biology, but about the colour of the buses in downtown Shanghai.

In the sixth form I had to apply to university so I thought it was about time I found out something about each of the veterinary schools. My dad worked as a guard on the railways, which meant I could get free tickets to travel all over the country. None of the veterinary colleges interviewed potential students at that time, there were just too many applicants. But I wasn't going to let that stop me. I wrote to each of them in turn and told them when I would be coming to meet the dean or principal. The way I saw it, if I was ever going to stand a chance I had to meet the top man and convince him of how much I wanted to be a vet.

My travels were an education in themselves. In Glasgow I was greeted at Central Station by a middle-aged Scot in a duffle coat and a balaclava who announced that 'just around the corner there was a wee young lady who was just dying to meet me'. He grabbed me by the arm and pulled me in her direction. She was old enough to be my grannie and I was pretty sure the university hadn't sent her. She took one look at me and informed her duffle coated companion I was far too young but if I had enough cash I would do. I pulled away from them and ran like hell out of the station pursued by the bruiser in the balaclava who shouted, 'Come back, you little bugger' as I sprinted the length of Sauchiehall Street.

The following morning I presented myself at the veterinary school at Bearsden. The dean's assistant met me. We spent a pleasant hour discussing golf at St Andrews and the Isle of Skye. Two subjects of which, as a native Devonian I of course have an intimate knowledge. I can't remember if we talked about vets at all. The students were away on holiday so nothing much was happening. These days the veterinary school at Glasgow is the centre of some of the world's top research into AIDS and other viral diseases but on that fine spring morning such international academic pre-eminence, like my own veterinary career, was just a dream for the future.

At Edinburgh I got to know the dean and his secretary better than I had expected. The city was struck by an unseasonal blizzard which stopped everything in its tracks. The students and most of the staff were sent home and the three of us drank coffee all day till the thaw set in and I could leave for home. At

Liverpool the students were on strike. About what I can't remember but my guess is that it was grants. Students are, and always will be, short of cash. You don't muck about with their grants and get away with it. Crossing a picket line to choruses of 'Go home you bum, go home', I made my way to the dean's office. He was no fool; he'd taken the day off. His secretary apologised and gave me a whistle-stop tour which was a bit like having a day trip on the *Marie Celeste*. I spent the rest of the day on the picket line chanting 'Go home you bum' with the best of them. I could see I would enjoy being a veterinary student if only I could get a place. I couldn't wait to sit in!

I must admit I never expected to be a patient when I arrived at the Royal Veterinary College in London. I caught the tube to Mornington Crescent and walked the few hundred yards to Royal College Street. Suddenly my right eye started to hurt like mad. Tears streamed down my face as I blinked and winked my way towards the college.

'We've got a right one here, Bert.' The doorman grinned at his colleague. 'Sorry mate, we don't have a casualty department. We only treat animals, see.'

'I know, I'm hoping to be a vet myself. I've got an appointment with the principal but I think something's got into my eye.'

The doorman rang for the registrar, who came for me.

'I'll get a pathologist to look at that eye,' she said matter-of-factly. 'Here, this might help you till we get it seen to.' She gave me a large white handkerchief which I folded up and pressed against my eye. She then escorted me on a tour of the college. It took a while to get to see the pathologists. First we met the anatomists, then the biochemists, then the physiologists. They were all interested in my career plans; they were even more interested in the large white hankie and my swollen eye. Eventually we came to the pathology department and one of the technicians flushed out the grit with sterile saline. It still hurt and it took ages for the blinking and winking to stop. The college principal, Dr Betts, greeted me with some concern. It must have been hard holding a conversation trying not to notice my enormous hankie but he pretended not to. Somehow I must have impressed him because a few weeks later an offer of a place came through the post. I now had offers from Glasgow and London. Loads of people never get offered one place let alone two. All I had to do now was pass my exams.

The A-levels proved Mr Barkell right: I was not a natural scientist. He knew it and the examiners knew it. I passed biology all right – perhaps plants weren't so bad after all – but physics and chemistry were a disaster. There was only one thing to do; I would have to resit. I don't think I've ever worked so hard in my life. For six months I lived and breathed physics and chemistry. Just after Christmas I sat the exams again. Glasgow had said they would still take me if I improved my grades.

In due course: 'Hello, is that the Glasgow vet school? I've passed my exams at the grades you asked for.'

There was a pause.

'Oh hello there.' It was the dean's assistant. 'I'm sorry to tell you this, Mr Taylor, but there's been such a demand for student places we've had to raise our grades even higher. If only you had done a little better in physics.'

I was never going to do any better in physics. I put the phone down and cried. All that effort. For this.

The next day a letter arrived from the Royal Veterinary College. My new results were good enough for them. I was in by the skin of my teeth.

And now here I was four days after starting at university flat on my back in some north London isolation hospital feeling sicker than I ever had in my life.

'You have meningitis,' the consultant informed me reassuringly, 'and as if that isn't bad enough, you have hepatitis too.'

I was scared. People died of meningitis. And hepatitis, which affects the liver, was no joke either.

'You're lucky,' he continued. I couldn't think why. 'Your meningitis and hepatitis have been caused by glandular fever.'

'Glandular fever?'

'The kissing disease. It's very popular with students. We'll know for sure in a couple of days' time when you come out in red spots.'

'Why will I do that?' I asked, puzzled.

'Your doctor gave you an antibiotic, ampicillin, before you came into hospital. He thought it would help your infection. Remember, you had a temperature?'

I remembered all right. You could have cooked an egg on my forehead.

'People who are given ampicillin when they have glandular fever break out in red spots seven days later. I'll be back in a couple of days with a camera to take a photo of yours.'

If you buy the *Wolfe Medical Atlas of Dermatology* and look up glandular fever or mononucleosis, its proper clinical name, you'll find a picture of a naked yellow body. Mine. Hepatitis causes jaundice. I am covered in red spots. It is, as they say, not a pretty sight. You can't see my face in the photo but I know it's me.

The consultant was delighted. The red spots had confirmed his diagnosis and he had got his snapshot. He had just told me I would soon get better and there was nothing now to stop me becoming a vet. It's a pity you can't see my face. You don't often see a smile that big!

3

'Pit bulls don't take prisoners!'

That's right, Dougie, give it to them straight, I thought as I listened to the afternoon phone-in on Radio Devon in the car.

'I know all about dogs.'

And didn't we know it too, Doug. I was beginning to think no one else in the whole world knew as much about dogs as Douglas Mossop. He was everywhere. If you turned on the television Douglas was there pointing out the perils of the pit bull and showing you how any dog attack could be avoided. 'You just have to be dominant, that's all,' he would snarl assertively, 'think dominant. You're the leader of the pack.' That old song by the Shangri-lahs couldn't have put it better! He was all over the newspapers. The *Evening Herald* ran his life story: 'Dominating dogs down the decades – a canine behaviourist looks back'.

And here he was again, the expert in full throttle, giving David Bassett and his *Afternoon South West* audience a quick Freudian analysis of the family pet turned danger dog. I was beginning to think the whole country was going dog crazy. There had been several really bad attacks on children. All sorts of family pet were involved but when it came to inflicting serious damage, the pit bull was in a class of its own. Not that anyone should have been surprised, really. After all, if you breed a dog for dog fighting then it is pretty obvious it's not going to be the number one choice for family pet. The thing that was really worrying was the sheer unpredictability of the dogs' behaviour. That's why Douglas and a hundred and one other canine psychoanalysts were such media darlings. Perhaps understanding dogs' behaviour could explain the attacks and help prevent them.

'I've been training dogs for twenty years or more and I haven't met one yet who's beaten me,' he had informed me when we first met. I could see why. He was over six foot tall and built like the Incredible Hulk. You'd have to be a pretty reckless rottweiler to argue with Douglas. If he'd thrown a stick for me I probably would have fetched it.

I wasn't surprised when almost overnight he magically transformed himself into a canine behaviourist. Canine counselling was catching on in a big way. Nobody wanted to be a dog trainer anymore. Dog training had echoes of Barbara Woodhouse. No, you couldn't go around blowing up animals' noses. As Dougie was forever telling me and everyone else, you had to get inside their minds.

I've often thought that orthopaedic surgery – especially in dogs – is a bit like playing with a rather expensive Meccano kit. You get all the metal plates, the pins and the screws, and with a little, or a lot, of fiddling around, magically from a jigsaw of uneven, spiky pieces you transform and repair a shattered limb. Marvellous. Mind you, it can be a bit of a game. For one thing it doesn't matter how many surgery or anatomy textbooks you read, you can bet the fracture you're having to deal with doesn't look a bit like any one of them. Of course there are some veterinary surgeons who make it look so easy that they've probably finished off and gone home for lunch while you're still scrubbing up. Sad to say, I'm not one. Orthopaedics can be very satisfying but, goodness me, I find it a struggle sometimes.

I was certainly struggling with Moss's injured leg. In fact I was beginning to wonder if I was ever going to make sense of all the bits and pieces that were once his left femur and tibia.

Moss, the red setter, is what you might call an incurable romantic. He's nearly fifteen but he still falls in love at the drop of a hat. Most of the time he's a pretty sensible chap and his owner Mrs Bryant adores him. Trouble is, if there's a bitch in season anywhere nearby Moss switches to autopilot and he's off. Usually he's away for days camped outside his beloved's home like some overeager bargain hunter queuing early for the January sales. Then, sometimes delighted, sometimes disappointed, always weary, he'll wander back into Mrs Bryant's life and she'll have him back as if nothing has happened.

But not this time. Moss fell for a farm dog who lived on the wrong side of the A38. For days he'd leave his Plympton home early in the morning and moon about outside the Lyneham Arms like some lovestruck teenager. From the Lyneham it was a quick hundred yards dash, across four lanes of speeding traffic, and his devotion would be rewarded. Like most dogs he never bothered to read the highway code, so, suddenly, when temptation had finally got the better of him, he rushed headlong in pursuit of love. The Ford Sierra that hit him didn't stand a chance. It skidded to a halt and Moss bounced off the bonnet and lay motionless in the central reservation.

'Come on old boy. Time to go home,' I said as I gently lifted him into my car for the quick ride back to the surgery. 'You're getting far too old to go chasing younger women.'

Slowly, deliberately, he wagged his tail, and I knew he was going to be all right.

And now, the following morning, here I was busily trying to put him back together again. His femur was split in two. A metal pin would put that right, but lower down the leg his tibia was shattered almost beyond repair. Screwing a metal plate to it was seeming more and more impossible as the damaged fragments of bone splintered. The last thing I needed was a phone call from the police.

'There's a pit bull gone berserk in Colebrook. The police think they might have to shoot it. They've called out the Royal Marines but they'd like you to be there just in case you can tranquillise it,' Linda, one of my nurses, informed me breathlessly.

'Oh great. How the hell am I going to get near it to

sedate it? They've got to be joking,' I said anxiously. I'd read about vets being called to ordinary dogs, family pets, that had suddenly gone bananas. Pretty dangerous if you asked me. It was happening to vets all over the country and now it was my turn. 'I've got to see to Moss first. But tell them I'll be there as soon as I can.' I paused. 'And Linda, I don't want to be the only dead hero. You're coming with me.'

It took a while, but gently and carefully I worked at Moss's leg until at last he had the kind of repair Barry Sheen would have been proud of. Very soon he would come round from his anaesthetic. My other nurses would take care of him then but right now Linda and I had to dash, the police were getting desperate. The pit bull was out of control.

'It's been like that for about an hour now. None of us can get near it,' Colin Trout, our local RSPCA inspector, informed me agitatedly. 'It's a right bugger. I reckon we'll have to shoot it.'

We had made our way round to the back of the house. Every few minutes a snarling brown furry figure would launch itself at the kitchen window, terrifying anyone who came near. The police were taking no chances. They were still sitting in their squad car. And I might have been wrong but I could have sworn that there, sitting in the back seat, was Douglas Mossop. But strangely, just for once he didn't have much to say for himself. In fact he seemed rather preoccupied and perhaps a little pale.

'Douglas came with the police,' Colin told me. 'Seems he's teaching them a bit about dog behaviour these days. This dangerous dog problem's rapidly getting out of hand and they need all the help they can get.'

Suddenly, without warning, Ellie, the pit bull, had turned on her owners and their three children. I'd met Ellie a few months before when she'd been ill with an upset stomach. I remembered her because I hadn't been paid a penny for her treatment.

'We'll be in on Monday to settle up, Mr Taylor,' the Smarts had said as they left the surgery. 'We're ever so grateful.' I hadn't held my breath. It's always seemed strange to me that people can spend £300 or more on a dog like a pit bull and then mysteriously run out of cash when their pet's ill. But then as my friends who work for the PDSA (People's Dispensary for Sick Animals) tell me, it's a strange world.

Mrs Smart had bundled her children out of the house and slammed the back door behind her. Ellie hadn't bitten anyone yet but from the way she was behaving that was just sheer luck. When they heard Mrs Smart screaming for help the neighbours had rung for the police. With Douglas's help they'd tried to subdue Ellie but that hadn't been a big success. Somehow Colin and I were going to have to catch her or she would be shot.

'Any bright ideas?' the police sergeant enquired as Colin and I stood discussing what to do next. 'I reckon we'll have to storm the building.'

Now, I've never stormed a building in my life. I'd seen the end of the Iranian embassy siege on television years ago but they'd had the SAS, and Kate Adie giving a blast-by-blast account. Somehow I didn't think Colin, Linda and I were in the same league.

'Right Colin, I'll go in first with my dog catcher,' I said authoritatively as if I did this sort of thing every day. 'I'll see if I can loop it over her head and catch her tight. You follow close behind and see if you can grab her with yours. Linda's ready with a sedative injection once we've caught her. For God's sake don't let go or we've all had it.' Dog catchers are long hollow poles with a loop of nylon cord at one end. Once you've caught a dog in the loop you tighten the cord and it can't get away. The pole's about six foot long, so, in theory, a raging pit bull shouldn't be able to get near enough to do any damage. I'd soon find out.

Gingerly I pushed open the back door and pushed the pole of the catcher through. There was a moment's silence as the dog, surprised by this invasion, summed things up. Then with a deafening snarl she came straight for me. This was no time to be gentle. Using the catcher like a spear I defended myself and poked and prodded her, growling and whining, back through the devastated kitchen and on through a passageway into the front room. The house was a mess. She had smashed and chewed her way through any door she had found closed. Curtains dangled in tatters from the windows. Cushions lay ripped around the rooms and children's toys were scattered everywhere. I had never realised a dog could do so much damage.

Colin and I edged her back into a corner. While he distracted her I was able, at last, to loop the dog catcher over her head. Colin secured her too and as we held her pressed to the floor not daring to let go for one moment, Linda injected a powerful sedative into her hind leg. We had her.

Within a few minutes Ellie was calm and starting to doze off. As she lay there gently snoozing it was hard to imagine that only a short time before she'd caused so much devastation. The police sergeant was taking no chances.

'I'd like you to put her down, Mr Taylor. I'm afraid she's too big a risk to the public. We were lucky this time, no child was injured, but we can't take the chance that this might happen again. Mrs Smart agrees.'

It took only a few moments for the intravenous injection to work and Ellie was gone. In spite of everything you couldn't help but feel sorry for her.

As Linda and I were about to drive back to the surgery, Colin came over to my car.

'Thanks, mate. I'm glad you came. Things were getting out of hand. And Dougie wasn't much help.' Come to think of it I'd almost forgotten about Douglas. He was still in the back of the police car, unusually quiet. 'He went in the house with the police and tried to reason with the pit bull.'

'What? Dominate it, you mean?' I asked interestedly. 'He's always going on about dominating dogs.'

'Yes I know, but not this time. She was too quick for him.'

'You mean she bit him?'

The RSPCA inspector shrugged his shoulders and flashed me a knowing smile.

'Oh yes, she bit him all right. She bit him, right in the balls!'

4

You might think that living on the edge of Dartmoor I'd be like most vets and associate the coming of spring with sheep. Hundreds of them. Cheviots and Blackfaces. Dartmoors and Devon Longwools. All dropping lambs quicker than you can blink. One big outdoor maternity ward from bleak old Princetown to the lusher pastures of the lovely South Hams. But no, for me spring hasn't arrived until Rambo Dean has woken up.

'Rambo's here for his vitamin injection, Mr Taylor,' Mrs Dean, his owner, informed me breathlessly. 'He does so look forward to coming to see you as soon as he comes out of hibernation. Look, he's smiling. See.'

Actually it was more of a grin than a smile but I knew what Mrs Dean meant. Most tortoises are shy retiring chaps but not Rambo. It was head out, shake it all about and grin at the vet. I grinned back.

Don't ask me why, but I often find you can communicate with tortoises if you rub noses with them. You might say it brings them out of their shell and they relax. I've never tried it with an Eskimo but I'm told they respond to nasal body language in much the same way.

'I'm worried about rustlers, Mr Taylor. There's been a few tortoises gone missing in Plympton and you know I'm concerned they'll be heading over to us in Plymstock soon.'

I'd heard quite a lot about tortoise rustling. Hooded men driving around the lanes late at night and jumping over garden fences for a quick rummage in the undergrowth before pushing off with a precious pet. With tortoises worth a few hundred pounds each it was getting to be big business.

Thousands of tortoises used to be imported into Britain from Greece and the Mediterranean. It was a pretty terrible trade. Stacked in wooden boxes, many died and many of the poor unfortunates who made it to the pet shops were so weakened and ill that they didn't last long in our much colder climate. I can remember taking a trip to the veterinary centre at Heathrow Airport when I was a student and seeing crate after crate of diseased and dying tortoises. I wasn't surprised when the trade was stopped and the import of tortoises banned. But it's made the ones that are here very valuable. In fact sometimes when I'm having a tortoise clinic at my surgery I feel more like an antiques valuer than a veterinary surgeon when I'm asked to put a price on some marvellous old bruiser who's been around since grandad was a boy. I like tortoises.

'Of course Rambo isn't an only tortoise,' Mrs Dean continued. 'I've got seven others, but he's my favourite. And do you know, I think he knows it too!'

Rambo's grin grew wider. He knew it, all right.

Rambo was put back in his box and one by one the others were presented to me for inspection and injection.

'Here's Mungo, Mary and Dorothy. All girls.' The girls glared at me one by one and then proceeded to relieve themselves of a whole winter's waste products as I gave them their vitamins.

'Lovely. Just lovely,' I murmured. 'Bring on the boys.'

'You've seen Rambo. So we've just got Stanley, Graham, Rupert and Arthur to attend to. Arthur is the shy one.'

Mrs Dean was right. In all the years I've known him, I've never once seen him come out of his shell. I'm no animal behaviourist, but I'm convinced Arthur is agoraphobic. Mind you, with Rambo and the others around it can be anything but a quiet life.

It's not too bad in early spring when the days and the nights are still a bit cool, but by high summer all hell breaks loose in Mrs Dean's garden.

'The neighbours have complained about the noise, I'm afraid,' Mrs Dean informed me a few months later as I stood in her garden and watched the frantic scenes around me. 'It's the shells bonking together like that all day, they object to.' I could see why. As Rambo launched headlong into Mary and ricocheted off her onto Dorothy there was a great crack of carapace. Stanley, Graham and Rupert were diving into anything that moved too. Only Arthur remained aloof, silent inside his shell as always. He didn't know what he was missing. There was an awful lot of

26

bonking going on in Mrs Dean's garden. 'They're like this from dawn to dusk whenever it's warm. What can I do?'

Actually a cold shower wouldn't have been a bad idea. You see, tortoises' behaviour is very temperature dependent. The hotter it is the livelier they get. You and I, we work the other way, which if you could have seen the fun they were all having, is a pity.

I shrugged my shoulders. I had no easy solution. 'Perhaps they'll just get bored and give it all up,' I suggested helpfully. 'No one's ever tried neutering a tortoise.'

I should have known better. The summer got warmer and warmer and the tortoise ballet grew ever more adventurous and noisy. The next-door neighbour took to playing his radio loudly whenever he was out gardening. The tortoises didn't seem to notice. They had more important things on their minds.

'Mr Taylor, it's Rambo. He's had a terrible accident.' Mrs Dean was sobbing down the phone. 'It's all my fault. I'm usually so careful. The lawnmower, I was using the lawnmower and I, I ran him over. He's bleeding badly. I think he's lost a leg.'

She was right. One of his back legs had been caught in the blades of the mower and had been sliced off in an instant. 'I think he'll be all right, Mrs Dean. Once he's over the shock I'll operate on him and stitch up his wounds,' I said when I'd had a chance to examine him.

It took about a day for his grin to come back and I

27

then decided he'd be fit enough for surgery. The only problem was I had to anaesthetise him first.

It isn't easy to anaesthetise a tortoise. For one thing, *you* try finding and raising a vein to inject into. Dogs and cats are pretty easy; give them a cuddle, clip away some fur from the foreleg, and away you go. Rabbits aren't bad. They've got great veins in their ears. But tortoises, no. Tortoises play hard to get. And there isn't much point in trying to mask them down with a few whiffs of halothane. All they do is pull back into their shells and hold their breath. It's a bit like trying to anaesthetise a pasty. And even when you do get an anaesthetic into them, the fun still isn't over. Their metabolism is so slow that where you can expect the average cat or dog to be sound asleep within seconds, you've got to be a little more patient with a tortoise. About a hour after you inject them you might, if you're lucky, get a yawn. Ninety minutes and counting, you might get doze-off. The great thing about tortoises is you can never tell.

The textbooks tell you there is a big venous sinus just above the tail, under the shell. Using the finest needle that would penetrate Rambo's hard skin, I injected our usual cat anaesthetic, Saffan, into it. The textbook was right, a trace of blood told me I was in the right place. All I had to do now was wait and hopefully Rambo would go to sleep. It took a while. Before he yawned I managed to spey two cats and stitch up a border collie who'd tangled with some barbed wire. Twenty minutes later, he was sound asleep and snoring. I'd never seen an anaesthetised tortoise before. His whole body relaxed and he became so floppy I felt sure he would fall out of his shell.

I carried him to the operating table and gently tidied up his wounds and stitched him back together again. Most dogs and cats come around in ten to fifteen minutes. Rambo took four hours. I kept him warm and gradually he became stiff and tortoiselike again. His grin was a bit lopsided and I was convinced he had a hangover.

'I don't like to see him limping, Mr Taylor. Is there nothing we can do to help him get around a little easier?' Mrs Dean wanted only the best for Rambo.

'I've got an idea, Mrs Dean. There was an amputee tortoise on the television not so long ago. They solved his problem with a Lego wheel and some superglue.'

'Anything, Mr Taylor. Anything.'

We tried it. I stuck a flat piece of Lego to the underside of Rambo's shell and snapped a wheel onto it. It worked a treat.

Almost immediately he was whizzing round Mrs Dean's garden with a turn of speed Nigel Mansell would have been proud of. Even the next-door neighbour was impressed although Mrs Dean rejected his suggestion to paint 'Go Faster' stripes on Rambo's shell. The female tortoises loved it. Rambo would round them up and career into them at high speed whilst the other boys were nowhere to be seen.

There was only one problem. When it comes to understanding tortoise love lives I am no Claire Rayner, but it was pretty obvious that Rambo was not as happy as he should have been.

'I think he's getting frustrated, Mr Taylor. Any time he gets in close for a cuddle with one of the girls, he starts to roll back because of his wheel. He doesn't grin anymore. How can we help him?'

The answer was simple. And now on hot summer days when the temperature rises and Rambo and the boys become amorous, Mrs Dean unclips the Lego bricks and takes his wheel off. He ambles a little more slowly over to the girls but they wait patiently whilst he performs with passion. His grin is back. He is a happy tortoise. If only Arthur knew what he is missing.

'And do you know, Mr Taylor,' Mrs Dean confided in me, 'it's a funny thing but I'm sure the girls find him more attractive since the accident.'

I thought of the limping tortoise and the Lego wheel that had transformed his life. 'It shouldn't be so surprising, Mrs Dean. Women always prefer a man with his own transport!'

5

Christmas came early to Dorset that year. Some of the coldest weather in twenty years brought the kind of snow I thought you only saw in Canada. Out along the coast, on the Bridport road, great gusts of wind piled the snowdrifts high and stopped the traffic for days. The whole county had become one enormous living Christmas card, and I loved it.

'You're late. In fact, you're bloody late. I've had thirty calves waiting for you for nearly two hours now. Where the bloody hell have you been?' Harry Jago, I could tell, was not pleased.

I've been late ever since I was born. And I was two weeks late for that. Ask my mum. It's not intentional, but over the years I've come to realise that my biological clock seems to run on a flat battery. No matter how hard I try I'm always behind time. Mind you, in a job like mine, sometimes you can't help it. There's always the unexpected call to catch you out.

I've always fancied myself as a bit of a rally driver. Most country vets do. And as I slithered and skidded through the snow on the road to Cerne Abbas I couldn't help thinking that with just a little more practice I could win next year's RAC dead easy.

Flying Finns were no match for high speed vets. I had a busy afternoon at Harry Jago's lined up. Thirty calves to disbud and castrate. Poor buggers. As if it wasn't bad enough losing your horns.

These sessions were always a bit like the Calgary stampede. Calves belting around the barn in every direction whilst Harry Jago's farmhands tried to catch them. As his men had usually just spent most of their lunchtime down the Royal Oak it was no contest. The calves would win every time and take ages to round up. Still, the exercise would do me good and I'd at least be keeping warm.

First, though, I had to have a quick look at Tim Sweet's pig. She'd farrowed the day before and now wasn't at all well. Her milk had dried up and Tim was sure she had mastitis. He was certain he was going to lose her and all the piglets. That was a loss he couldn't afford.

In fact the way things were going Tim was only just hanging on to being a farmer by the skin of his teeth. He'd spent a few years working for Harry and a few others and when he got the chance to rent an empty barn in the village he'd jumped at it. The place was now full of all sorts of animals. A few sheep, a couple of goats, half a dozen young cattle and Bathsheba, Tim's saddleback pig.

'She's in a bad way. I do hope you can help her and the little 'uns,' Tim said as I was putting on my boots and rummaging about in the back of the car for some antibiotic and a syringe and needle. 'She's kind of special to me.'

He slid back the huge door to the barn and we went inside. Bathsheba was lying on her side in a makeshift pen Tim had put together for her. She couldn't have cared less about her piglets. She just lay there moaning and gasping as they tried in vain to suckle her. It was so cold in the barn that I felt sure the poor things would die of hypothermia, even if we could get Bathsheba to feed them again. There was so little bedding in her pen that there was nowhere they could huddle for warmth. They obviously had spent most of their young lives struggling for survival on cold slimy concrete.

'I'll give her some antibiotic to deal with her infection,' I said encouragingly. 'Oxytocin, as pituitary hormone, will encourage her to let down her milk, but we've really got to do something to get these piglets warm or else we'll lose the lot.'

'I've got a bit of hay and straw left,' Tim replied. 'I was saving it for the cattle and the sheep. I can't afford any more until after Christmas. But I suppose they'll have to have it.'

'It's either that or you can kiss them goodbye.'

Tim went to the other end of the old, draughty barn to get what bedding he could and I started to look around at some of the other animals.

My heart sank.

The young cattle, two Herefords, a few Galloways and some South Devons were in a terrible state. They were over a year old but lack of proper feeding and daylignt had left them stunted and underdeveloped.

33

Every one of them wheezed and coughed and most were covered in ringworm.

'God, Tim,' I cried, 'what's been going on here? These poor bloody things haven't got a chance. They deserve better than this.'

'I know, I know. But the whole thing's hopeless. I can't afford to rent any grazing and I've been trying to bring in all the food they need. I can hardly afford that now.'

Working part time on the farms brought in a bit. Relief milking, silage making and harvesting were Tim's main jobs but with a family at home to look after as well there wasn't much cash or much time left to look after the animals.

'You mean they never see the sun or get any fresh air?'

'No, I've no fields. So they never get out.'

The dark December afternoon grew darker as I looked around this awful prison that was the animals' only home. I did what I could but it took ages. The goats and the sheep needed their feet trimmed. They also needed a good feed. They were so painfully thin. I gave each of the cattle an antibiotic injection which would at least give them some relief from their respiratory infections. And Bathsheba, poor Bathsheba, would she and her piglets make it through the night? God only knew.

The senior partner of the practice was not happy when I returned back from my afternoon's work.

'I've had Harry Jago on the phone. Seems you kept him waiting for hours. He's not amused.'

I explained that I was sorry but that the condition of Tim Sweet's animals had really concerned me. I just had to do something for them.

'I'll take a look out there myself in the morning and see if things are as bad as you say, and we'll go from there.'

We went from there all right. Next morning the senior partner was seething as he came back from Tim's.

'I've never seen anything like it. How on earth have things been allowed to get so bad out there? I'm ringing the ministry to see if there's anything they can do.'

I met the ministry vet at Tim's barn that afternoon. 'Look', he said after he'd had a good look all around the place, 'I want you out here every day for the next couple of weeks to make sure things improve. I've made Mr Sweet very aware of his responsibility towards these animals. I'll be back to check on things in a few days. See you then.'

I was just about to get in the car when one of the villagers who lived in a cottage near the barn came across to me.

'Thank goodness somebody is doing something about those animals at last. Everyone here has been so concerned for months. They never go out and I'm sure they never get enough to eat. I don't think Mr Sweet can afford to look after them properly. Is there anything we in the village can do to help?' As if by magic, from that moment things started to improve. Hay and straw appeared from nowhere and over the next few days the barn was transformed. Everyone mucked in and the dark, damp and dingy pens took on a new life. Trailers loaded down with animal feed arrived and the animals tucked in like there was no tomorrow. Tim was overwhelmed.

'I never knew people could be so kind,' he told me on Christmas Eve. 'The ministry vet was out yesterday and he was delighted. He was amazed at the improvement.'

So was I. I was even more amazed when the next tractor that arrived was Harry Jago's piled high with bales of sweet-smelling hay.

'These are for you Tim. I'd no idea you'd got yourself in so much trouble, old son. I'm sure I can find you some land so you can turn your stock out later in the year.' He smiled and continued loudly, 'Oh and there's one more thing Tim: Merry Christmas.'

The next day I called on Tim and a few of the village children as they scurried round the barn tending to the animals. The sheep and goats lay contentedly, ruminating slowly in their pens. Not a cough or a wheeze could be heard from any of the cattle and their coats were improving as the ringworm started to clear. But best of all was the squeaking and the squawking coming from Bathsheba's pen. Looking at her and her eight piglets you'd have hardly believed that not so long ago their lives had hung in the balance.

'Aren't you missing your Christmas dinner, Mr Taylor?' Tim asked as I sat on a hay bale in the middle of the barn just taking it all in and thinking of the wonderful changes that had happened in so short a time because, just once, people had really cared.

'No Tim. Right now, I'm just glad to be here.'

6

It's not every day you get kicked in the face by an ostrich. Not that a little thing like that would stop Fernley Slee for one moment. As he was fond of telling me himself, 'You never know what's coming next in our game, boy. You've just got to be prepared that's all. Be prepared.'

I was spending time with Fernley during my holidays from the Royal Veterinary College. For the first two years of our course whilst we studied hard to make sense of anatomy, physiology, biochemistry and pharmacology, we didn't get much chance to spend time with real animals. Most of the ones we saw were either pickled in formalin or had been dead so long only their bones remained, held together by blue tack. Well, at least Foxhunter's accessory carpal is. I didn't mean to pull it off, honest. It sort of came away in my hand. You'd never notice, though. A blob of blue tack and with a bit of building up, I'm sure he could win an Olympic gold again tomorrow.

Being with Fernley was being in the real world where animals lived, breathed and belted you in the teeth if you upset them.

Mind you, ostriches do get upset easily.

Plymouth at that time had a zoo, right in the middle of town at Central Park. It wasn't much of a zoo really, more a quarantine holding station for the large numbers of giraffes, lions, tigers and other animals that were being imported from Africa and elsewhere to form the big safari parks like Longleat which were becoming so popular. Part of Fernley's job was to visit Plymouth zoo regularly and look after the health of the animals. And as I was seeing practice with him, Daktari time for Fernley was Daktari time for me too.

'These tiger cubs seem pretty big to me, Mr Slee,' I said anxiously one afternoon as I struggled with a stethoscope to listen to the chest of a real growler. 'How old are they when they become unsafe to handle?'

'Oh, about three or four months.'

'How old did you say these chaps were?'

Fernley thought about it for one moment. Then with a sly grin to one of the keepers he answered, 'Well, Nigel, these boys are about six months. Don't worry though, they've just been fed.'

There are times when you just know your patient is so healthy, a protracted clinical examination isn't necessary. This was one of them. I made my excuses and left. Quickly.

Fernley of course had been outside the tigers' pen all the time and as he watched me struggle out of their cage faster than Houdini in overdrive a giant smile broke across his face and he laughed himself silly.

'All good experience, boy. All good experience.'

39

One thing was sure. Fernley loved a joke. For a long time he kept a chimpanzee as a pet at his practice. When new pharmaceutical reps called, they'd be invited upstairs to wait and have a cup of tea while Fernley carried on with surgery. The chimpanzee would come as a complete surprise. Some reps would try and ignore it and sipped away anxiously as they waited for what seemed an age for Fernley to join them. The chimpanzee was a prize mimic and would return sidelong glances and stares with gleeful enthusiasm. Occasionally it would be overcome with affection for its teatime guest and Fernley would climb the stairs to find it sitting on an unsuspecting lap, cuddling the bemused caller like some long-lost simian sidekick.

'Tell me you can see him too, Mr Slee, or else I'm sure the firm will pull me off the job,' the man from Beechams had pleaded, keeping his eyes tightly closed as the chimp embraced him in an amorous armlock. Fernley fell about.

Fernley Slee wasn't a veterinary surgeon but a veterinary practitioner. Nowadays when all of us have to have university degrees there aren't many practitioners left. Fernley spent only a few years at the Royal Veterinary College and left without completing the course. Back in the thirties that didn't stop you from putting up your plate and getting on with being an animal doctor. Fernley had set up practice in Plymouth and had soon started to build up a larger-than-life reputation.

When Plymouth was almost destroyed during the wartime Blitzes Fernley turned out time and time again to help the unfortunate animals caught up in it. Not far from Millbay Station a stable full of horses used by the Great Western Railway suffered a direct hit when the Luftwaffe smashed the town. Their stable became a fireball. Fernley did what he could but many of the horses were hurt beyond hope and as Plymouth burnt around him, one by one he shot those who didn't have a chance.

Sometimes he was luckier. Fearing a very bad air raid, he decided to evacuate the animals in his surgery, then in the centre of town, to Plympton, on the outskirts. He bundled them into the back of his car and drove as quickly as he could out of town. As he was leaving, the raid started and what followed was a hair-raising journey through the night as all around him the Blitz raged. Next day he returned to the devastated heart of the town. There was no surgery; just a few bricks where it had been. Fernley would have to start again.

And start again he did. His practice became very successful. If there was a new operation or a new procedure that Fernley had read about somewhere he'd be the first to try it. Soon the other vets in the town would be calling to find out more about this new technique to repair cruciate ligaments or remove a prolapsed disc that they'd heard Fernley had been trying. He had always been interested in circus and zoo animals and as time went by he found himself involved more and more in treating elephants, lions and all the other wild and wonderful creatures that used to be part of the big circuses. In those days Billy

Smart's, Chipperfield's and best of all Bertram Mills would have their own circus trains and once they arrived at North Road Station they'd have a giant parade through the town to the big top.

Fernley loved it. Hippos with toothache, giraffes with bad colds, you couldn't beat him. Chances were if you strolled into any visiting menagerie in the whole of the South West it wouldn't be too long before you spotted the vet with the handlebar moustache and the E-type Jaguar. Fernley Slee at work.

When the ostrich kicked him in the face, the moustache came in handy.

'You need stitches in that upper lip,' the surgeon in Casualty had told him.

'If you think you're going to shave off my moustache, boy, you've got another bloody think coming.'

The surgeon quickly thought again.

'You know, sometimes with young children we use their own hair tied gently together when they've suffered head wounds. Works just as well as stitches. Perhaps we could use your moustache in much the same way?'

'Bloody get on with it then, boy,' Fernley had retorted.

The surgeon got on with it.

Next morning I'd thought it had been quiet whilst I was helping Fernley operate. Usually every time I picked up the wrong instrument I'd soon realise my mistake as a torrent of lighthearted abuse hit me.

'Not the bloody Allis forceps, boy. I need a bloody pair of artery forceps.' The offending Allis forceps would hurtle skywards a few inches above my head. 'Get it bloody right.'

I use much the same technique when I'm training new theatre nurses. I don't have Fernley's authority, though, and they just laugh.

You didn't laugh at Fernley.

But this morning he wasn't saying much at all. All I'd get every now and then was a few exasperated mumbles as I fiddled with a swab or reached for some new suture.

Eventually his wife put me in the picture.

'Yesterday evening Fernley had to go to the zoo urgently. One of the ostriches was ill with a swollen foot. Silly bugger only tried to pick it up and look at it like it was a horse. Next minute, wham, and he's flat on his back spitting out teeth. And the number of times I've heard him tell you to be prepared.'

Fernley smiled disconsolately and pointed at his mouth. I could see his moustache holding his upper lip together. No wonder he wasn't saying much.

As an ostrich handler perhaps he wasn't much good but when it came to helping any young person like me who wanted to become a vet then Fernley was in a class of his own. I'd gone to him whilst I was still at school and explained the difficulty I was having in getting a place at veterinary school.

'If you really want it, boy, you'll do it. You can be sure of that,' he had said encouragingly. 'But it's bloody hard work and when you come out of college it doesn't stop there.'

When I did get in he had been delighted. 'Open

house, boy, open house. Whenever you want to come and see a bit of practice I'll be here. Just come, boy. Just come.'

So, like a hundred other youngsters over the years I went to spend time with him. I learnt a lot about the things they were trying to tell us about at college but most of all I learnt that being a vet is the best job there is in the world if you bring as much love and enthusiasm to it as Fernley has over the years.

Not so long ago the president of the Royal College of Veterinary Surgeons came to Plymouth. He held a meeting for all the local vets in the Holiday Inn. It was a fine evening and gave us all a chance to discuss current issues in the veterinary world. You could write a question down and pass it in to the president for him to answer. I filled in my slip, but I knew my query wouldn't be answered that evening.

About six months later Fernley Slee was invited to the College in London. It was, he told me later, the proudest day of his life. Although he had a very successful practice he had no formal qualifications, but they had awarded him an honorary associateship of the College in recognition of his lifetime's work.

The president hadn't let me down.

It was my way of saying thank you.

7

Roy Orbison was almost right. But it wasn't only the lonely who knew the way he felt tonight. There was a pig in the far north of Scotland who had a pretty good idea too.

I had been in the Highlands for a couple of weeks. Well, you've got to do something when you've just qualified as a vet and you're filling in time before you jet off to work at a Canadian university. My first locum had been in Dartford. The highlight of my stay there was a trip to see a horse with colic on Canvey Island. Compared to Canvey Island, Scotland sounded great.

'And where are you heading just now?' the guard had asked me when I boarded the train at Inverness.

'It's a small place called Rogart, somewhere north of Invergordon.'

'Aye, that's right. Just let me know when you want to get off and I'll stop the train for you.'

It was a very relaxed sort of train journey. Every now and then someone would wave us down and we would make a stop at a halt or station that as far as I could see had been closed down long before Dr Beeching was wielding his axe on Britain's railways.

None of them were mentioned in the timetable but it didn't seem to matter; no one bothered about the timetable anyhow. This was the Highland way of doing things.

'You'll have a wee dram while you're waiting,' the guard had said when we reached Rogart. 'Mr Hadrian's always a few minutes late to pick up his locums. He waits until the train passes his surgery and then heads for the Highland Hotel. We take all his vets there.'

The Highland Hotel was soon full. All the passengers, the driver and the guard were having a great time until eventually someone remembered the train had to be in Thurso that evening. They'd better get a move on, there were more malts waiting. 'Not a word to British Rail mind,' Donald the driver whispered to me and raised his finger to his lips, as he collected the level-crossing keys from the landlord. 'Here's Mr Hadrian now. Good luck.'

Veterinary practice in the Highlands was certainly different. For one thing you had to travel so far to get to see your patients.

'I've a cow calving, can you come sometime today or tomorrow?'

'I'll be there as quick as I can. Where are you?'

'Kinlochbervie.'

'But that's about a hundred miles.'

'Oh at least. We'll be seeing you, then.'

And off I'd set. In midsummer there's hardly any darkness in the Highlands and I'd make my journeys to the remotest of crofts in broad daylight courtesy of the midnight sun.

Sometimes Anthony Hadrian would be away for days. A ferry to this island, a plane to that. If you liked travelling, the Highlands was the place to be.

'There's a pig I want you to see,' he announced to me one evening. 'I've got some blood testing to do up near Lochinver. Old James Snoddy has been trying to get a litter from his pig for ages. I'm not much good at artificial insemination.' He paused. 'You'll be OK though, just out of college. I've told him you're an expert.'

Snoddy's pig. God, I'd heard about Snoddy's pig on the train. Everyone from John O'Groats to Inverness knew about Snoddy's pig.

'Old Snoddy's a hard man, mind,' Murdo, the guard had told me. 'Not so long ago he chased a vet off his farm with a shotgun. Seems the vet wanted to blood test his cows. Mr Hadrian had to go back with a police escort. Snoddy said he had no bloody cows and all vets were bloody parasites anyway.'

Donald the driver had added enthusiastically, 'Leave your engine running, laddie, and you'll be fine for a quick getaway. No, Snoddy doesn't love vets much. Loves his pig a lot though, so I've heard. You'll find out, I expect. Mr Hadrian sends all his vets there. You look after wee Dora, mind.'

Wee Dora was the biggest Large White pig I have ever met. In fact I'd be hard pressed to believe they made Large Whites any larger. Nothing was too good for James Snoddy's pride and joy. She had had all the food she ever wanted and had turned into a one-pig European pork mountain. She was huge.

'I want her pregnant, laddie. And I'm told you're just the man for the job. Get on with it.' James Snoddy, resplendent in Highland kilt, had announced when I arrived at his croft.

Getting a pig pregnant is largely a matter of timing. They come into season about once every three weeks and you have about forty-eight hours when she stands a chance of holding to service and becoming a mum. At least that's what the textbooks tell you. But they're talking about pigs that have company. If you're an only pig it plays havoc with your hormones. In big pig units they have a boar who does nothing much all day but mooch about posing like a rather tubby James Dean in a pen all to himself. He never gets to serve a sow. That's done artificially. He just smells manly and the girls go wild and come on heat. Beatlemania is nothing to a pig in love.

'I've got a boar spray,' James Snoddy informed me proudly. 'A few squirts of this stuff and you'll be fine.'

I'd heard about these boar sprays. Aftershave with an added punch. It was a bit like playing with fireworks. Spray a few whiffs of concentrated boar anywhere near a sow in season, then stand well back.

'And one more thing. Do you like Doris Day?'

'If I'm honest I'm more an Eric Clapton man myself,' I replied hesitatingly. 'You know, "Layla" and "I Shot the Sheriff".'

'Dora likes Doris. I've found if I play her a little

music on my wee tape recorder it pacifies her. Gets her in the mood you might say.'

Of course James Snoddy was right. Animals do respond to music. In fact I was sure I had read somewhere that if you wanted to improve your milk yield all you had to do was play music in the milking parlour. Cows love music. Apparently Pink Floyd's 'Dark Side of the Moon' works a treat though I'm not too sure how they'd respond to the Sex Pistols. Dry up, I expect. Cows are great critics.

'She loves, "Take me Home to the Black Hills".'

'"The Black Hills of Dakota"?'

'The very same.'

I have to admit that as I stood in that lonely Scottish barn and Doris sang, I could see by Dora's reaction that for her romance was in the air. Could be she'd heard the voice of the mystic mountains, or perhaps the boar spray was starting to get to her. It was certainly getting to me.

'You've got the inseminator?' James Snoddy asked at length. 'I've picked up the boar semen from the railway station. Had it sent Red Star from York.' James Snoddy was always having it sent Red Star from York. About once every month for the past two years. 'I'll just see if she's ready. If she is I'll change the tape and we can get started.'

'Doris done her job then?' I enquired patiently.

'Oh yes. My word yes. See how her eyes have glazed over. Now what she needs is Jimmy Shand.'

Of course. Why hadn't I thought of that. Jimmy Shand the pig breeder's favourite. Well, at least in the

Highlands. South of Watford you can get by with Barry Manilow at a pinch.

'"The Bluebell Polka". Just the job, laddie, just the job.' Snoddy shouted excitedly. 'I'll just see if she's still in season and we're off.'

To tell if a pig is in season is a fairly simple matter. All you do is jump on her and if she stands steady as a rock arching her back – lordosis the pig men call it – she's as ready for insemination, natural or otherwise, as she'll ever be. Jimmy Shand and his band were playing away furiously. With a hitch of his kilt James Snoddy launched himself into action. With a great thump he landed splat in the middle of Dora's back and for a moment she stood there, back arching ready for action. This, I thought, is too good to be true.

'Have you got your gadget, laddie?'

You have to have a bit of a knack using the 'gadget'. To inseminate a pig you need a long rubber tube which twirls spectacularly into rings at one end. This I'm told resembles a boar's penis. I'll take everyone's word for it. Early on in the history of pig insemination whoever designed the first rubber inseminators got the thread of the terminal coils wrong. Result: an instant rejection from affronted sows that nearly put pork off the nation's plates for a decade. But things had improved and my gadget was to the best of British standards. I could only hope Dora would be impressed. I loaded it with the semen, then all I had to do was inseminate Dora and I could go home.

Until then I had never danced the Bluebell Polka with anyone, never mind a pig being ridden by a

Scotsman in a kilt. One prod from me and Dora was off. Round and round the barn we sped. James Snoddy hung on grimly but it was no use, Dora had obviously had enough.

'What are you playing at, laddie? Get on wi' it.'

Easier said than done. A stationary pig is one thing. Trying to inseminate Dora was like trying to play darts on a surfboard.

'Not a chance,' I said breathlessly. 'She's obviously come out of season. We'll have to try again next time.'

As I drove away from the croft the melodious sound of Jimmy Shand and his band drifted across the Highland evening. Every now and then a cry of, 'I'll give you bloody Doris Day. Why don't you stand still, you wee madam. It's as if you don't want piglets' echoed out from the barn, followed by an anguished cry of 'Bloody parasites!'

As for me, I've never tried to inseminate a pig since.

8

The cardboard box on the back seat of my sister's car
began to wobble frantically. For a moment there was
a wild scrabbling going on inside and then trium-
phantly, as if by magic, a cat's head popped out
through the tattered top and started miaowing
furiously.

'This is Barnaby. He needs a home,' my sister
Vivian announced, knowing full well that in that
moment he had found one with me. I've always been
fond of cats and anyway, who could resist this tiny
silver-grey bundle, who, although he was probably
only a few months old, had obviously seen better
times? Vivian added with a smile, 'There's a lady in
our village who rescues cats. She thinks Barnaby was
hit by a car. One of his big front teeth is missing and
he walks a bit strangely but otherwise he's perfect.'

Barnaby did walk a bit strangely. He had what you
might call a John Wayne limp. The sort of gait
gunfighters in the wild west used to develop from
years of slinging heavy Colt .45s around their waists
and ambling up the main street of Dodge City just
before noon ready for a shoot out. In fact Barnaby
couldn't quite manage a straight line. He would

zigzag across the floor like a dinghy tacking wildly with the wind across Plymouth Sound.

I was pretty convinced he was brain damaged. He might have been concussed in a car accident, sure; after all, one of his canine teeth was missing; but I felt it was more likely he'd been born that way. Some cat viral diseases affect the cerebellum of the unborn kitten. You need a healthy cerebellum to balance properly. There was a good chance Barnaby was a farm cat. Vivian was living at Horrabridge, a small village on the edge of Dartmoor. Lots of cats lived there in the barns. Every few months a new litter of kittens would appear to take their chances with the rest. It was pot luck if they'd survive. Cat flu and feline infectious enteritis finished most of them off. If Barnaby's mum had been ill when she was carrying him then that would explain his problem. *Cerebellar ataxia* the textbooks call it, but that was just the way Barnaby was and it made you love him even more.

The next day I was leaving for Cornwall. I'd got a job with a practice in Helston, the home of the Floral Dance.

'I hope you've got your passport, son,' I called to Barnaby as we drove across the Tamar Bridge. 'The Cornish are very fussy who they let in to Cornwall you know. Mind you, you should be all right. With your stripy coat you look a bit like a mackerel. The Cornish love mackerel.'

The cat box remained silent. Barnaby wasn't amused. There are some cats who just can't take a joke.

As I settled into the daily routine of the Cornish practice, Barnaby's life was transformed. From stray to socialite. Even Eliza Doolittle would have been impressed by his rapid change of fortune.

Of course, everybody loved him. If anyone paid him the slightest bit of attention he would turn on the charm and the limp would become a little more easy to spot and the wobble just a touch more woeful. He became the darling of the coffee-morning circuit. I started to lose count of the number of homes he would disappear to for a quick meal. Children, especially the girls, would make a great fuss of him, and I'd often find him being wheeled about proudly in a pram piled high with dolls and cuddly toys. As long as he was the centre of attention he was happy. Soon, he had his own bowl of milk waiting for him every morning and afternoon at the local newsagents and if anyone in the street was holding a Tupperware party he'd be there poking through the plastic with the best of them. At night he'd sit with me and watch television. He was particularly fond of football and David Attenborough. He'd watch for hours entranced as Liverpool beat Arsenal or David scurried through the Amazon jungle scattering humming birds as he went. Barnaby particularly liked humming birds. One night as *Life on Earth* came to an end and the news appeared he went frantic and pawed at the television controls trying to get rid of the news and bring David back. He looked at me accusingly as the best he could come up with was Jan Leeming or snooker.

For lunchtimes Barnaby had discovered a builder's

hut in fields beyond my house. A new estate was being put up and every day six or seven of the builders would gather for sandwiches and pasties. Barnaby and the way he walked became a talking point. They'd been even more intrigued when they'd seen him return to my house every day when their lunchbreak ended.

'No, I told 'em, Mr Taylor. I said there was one thing you boys can be sure of. No vet would have a lash up of a cat like that,' Archie Bosustow informed me one night at the Blue Anchor. 'And he's a proper lash up too, I can tell you.' Archie then went on to perform a very good impersonation of Barnaby's lolloping gait. When he added, 'And he looks just like John Wayne on a bad day', I knew it was my cat he was talking about.

I spluttered on my pint and rather shamefacedly admitted that Barnaby was mine. I spent the next few weeks trying to avoid Archie.

This wasn't easy because as well as being a part time builder, he worked most evenings behind almost every bar in the town and also helped out at the local agricultural merchants. I was beginning to think everyone in Cornwall knew about my cat when one of our farm clients, miles away in Manaccan, greeted me when I arrived in his farmyard one morning with, 'Howdy pardner, I hear you're the vet who's got a cat who thinks he's a cowboy.'

The biggest thing that happens each year in Helston is the Furry Dance. To you, me and Terry Wogan it's the Floral Dance but the Helston people invented it, so they should know. It's supposed to be an ancient celebration of spring. Everyone dances in and out of each other's houses whilst the town band serenades them loudly. It's great fun and it's probably one of the best excuses the Cornish ever came up with for a party. Mind you, I think the best time to enjoy it is the week before, when, on the evening of the first of May, the town band and the locals have a practice. The town is decked out with bluebells and spring greenery from the nearby woods and for a couple of hours the magic of the Flora takes over and you feel time has stopped still.

Of course, Barnaby just had to be there. What, miss the high spot of Helston's social calendar? He'd followed a few of his young admirers down into the town and as they twirled around the ancient streets and the band played loudly I swear Barnaby joined in and lolloped away in time to the music as best he could.

'I've never seen a lash up dance like that,' Archie Bosustow cried to me enthusiastically as he caught sight of the cat in the midst of all the schoolchildren. 'You've been giving him lessons!'

I'm sure Barnaby missed Cornwall and all his friends when I moved back to Plymouth. For a while he seemed lost, and spent so much time around the house I was certain he'd never go out on the town again. He soon made up for it in a big way, though. Every night I'd let him out just before I went to bed, and I soon realised he'd found something better to do than stay with me. One evening I watched as he shot straight across the road to one of the neighbours and then started to miaow like mad until the front door was opened.

He was no fool. The girls who lived in the house were very pretty. In fact one of them, Sue, had been Miss Plymouth the year before. He'd made himself very much at home, lucky chap.

'Oh yes, we've been looking after Tiddles for some time now,' Sue said when I called to the door asking for Barnaby. 'I had no idea he was yours.'

'Tiddles' was sitting idly grooming himself on Sue's sofa. He was doing his best to ignore me. Traitor.

'When he first started coming to the house, we rushed him to the vet's because we thought he'd been run over. The vet couldn't find anything wrong with him but Tiddles doesn't half walk funny.'

'Yes,' I mumbled. This was no time to tell her I was a vet myself. 'He's been like that for years. Ever since he was a kitten. I was told it might be brain damage.'

His social life wasn't as hectic in Plymouth but with ladies like Sue to dote over you, life could have its compensations. He used to walk to the end of the street and watch me drive off to work before starting off on his morning round of social calls.

One morning he just disappeared. I never found him again. That's nearly ten years ago, but even now, every time a silver tabby comes into my surgery I give it a special check. I'm looking for a cat with one tooth missing and a limp like John Wayne. One day I'm sure I'll find him.

9

If I was going to have any chance at all of examining Snowy the hamster, the tractor and the cows would have to go. It's always the same when little David Kemp comes to the surgery. If he comes, his toys come too. Usually we play Masters of the Universe or Teenage Mutant Ninja Turtles before I get down to the serious business of giving Snowy or Floss his guinea pig a checkover. But today we had gone decidedly rural.

'I'm going to be a farmer when I grow up,' he informed me proudly. 'Do you like my tractor?'

'It's great. Just the job for all those muddy fields we've got round here. I bet there's lots of little boys who would love a tractor just like that. In fact I can think of one right now . . . a friend of mine who lives in Dorset.'

It was Sunday morning and as I drove out across the lush Dorset countryside I could see why Thomas Hardy had loved it so much. I was working in Dorchester, his Casterbridge, and I was fast beginning to realise I was living and working in one of England's loveliest counties. A patchwork of fields opened up below me as I took the steep road down to Roger Davey's farm. Beautiful. This was what being a country vet was all about.

'My dad says she's got milk fever. She only calved yesterday and today she can't seem to stand up properly. She's not eating either. What are you going to do, Mr Taylor?'

Roger's son Neil, all of six years old, was obviously in charge of things this morning. You could tell he was a farmer's son. Wellington boots, a waxed jacket and a tiny peaked cap. A proper country gentleman.

'Well son, I'll give her an injection of calcium and if I'm lucky she'll soon be fine again,' I told him. Milk fever isn't a fever at all. When cows calve and produce milk a lot of calcium suddenly leaves their bloodstream. This makes their muscles very weak and they find it hard to stand up. The treatment is simple. You give them an injection of calcium and they usually recover, sometimes dramatically. I once gave a bottle of calcium intravenously to a cow who was flat out on a moorland river bank. She responded, and no mistake. Up she jumped, splash, right into the River Dart. 'That was bloody impressive,' the farmer shouted as we watched her drift effortlessly downstream, 'but I'm buggered if I'm going to dive in after her. That's what I pay you for!'

Roger's cow didn't respond at all to the intravenous calcium I gave her. It seemed like milk fever, but I wasn't convinced. I checked her temperature and made sure she didn't have mastitis. Cows with really bad udder infections collapse too. I listened to her chest and abdomen carefully with my stethoscope. Normally you can hear a few burpings and gurglings as the cow ruminates. The odd belch tells you everything's all right but all I could hear was an odd tinkling sound as I listened to the left-hand side of her body.

'If it sounds like someone peeing on a tin roof from twenty yards,' a Canadian vet had once told me, 'then buddy, there's no doubt about it. That cow has got a displaced abomasum. And you have to do something about it.'

Cows have got four stomachs. One of them, the abomasum, usually sits on the right-hand side of the abdomen. But sometimes, especially round about calving, it can move and cause serious problems.

The funny thing was I'd been discussing displaced abomasums and what to do with them with a farmer I'd happened to meet in the practice car park. 'I've had a couple with displaced stomachs,' he'd said. 'God, it was a game and a half getting them better. First we rolled them about all over the place trying to shift it and in the end it took two vets, one each side, operating up to their armpits to put things right.'

Sometimes rolling a cow made the abomasum slide back where it belonged. A rough ride in the back of a lorry could help too. But if that didn't work you had to try surgery. The operation he described is a bit like a veterinary version of pass the parcel. One vet grabs the abomasum and hands it to the other to be stitched down so it can't move again. That sounds easy, but it can take ages and the cow doesn't enjoy it much. The farmer usually isn't that appreciative either as it is often a long time before his cows come back into milk.

'I know an easier way,' I announced happily. 'It's something I learnt in Canada. All you do is roll the cow on her back. Then you make a quick incision in her stomach and, bingo, the abomasum's right beneath your hand in its normal place. All you do then is stitch her up, making sure the abomasum is anchored in the wound. Some Canadian vets don't even bother to make an incision. They just run some linen thread right through where they think the abomasum will be,' I continued breathlessly.

'How long does this take?' the farmer enquired. 'My last cow was operated on for over two hours.'

I could just imagine the two vets feverishly feeling for the abomasum and trying time and again to slide the slippery organ with a life of its own to each other. No joke.

'About twenty minutes,' I informed him confidently. It was a confidence based on experience. I'd seen several cows operated on this way at the Ontario veterinary college and I'd soon learnt the technique. Mind you, any surgery is easy when you're talking about it, not doing it.

'You're going to operate, then,' Neil said as I explained what was wrong with his dad's cow. 'Oh good. Can I watch? I'm going to be a farmer one day you know, just like my dad.'

I suddenly realised Neil and I weren't alone. As I had been examining the cow Roger Davey had appeared at the door of the loose box and without disturbing me had listened to every word I had said. I recognised him at once. Roger was the farmer I had met in the car park.

'Right,' he said expectantly. 'You can fix one of these in twenty minutes. Now's your chance.'

Me and my big mouth. There is no such thing as an innocent conversation with a farmer. I'd dropped myself right in it.

The operation, as it turned out, was very much as I had described to Roger. With a bit of a struggle we turned her on her back and after infiltrating some local anaesthetic over the site of the incision, I prepared her with some antiseptic and surgical spirit and got on with it. Neil asked me loads of questions and watched with interest as I fished for the pink abomasum and stitched it neatly into place.

'Just under twenty minutes. Well done.' Roger beamed enthusiastically. 'Let's just hope you've cured her.'

As it turned out that's just what I did. Within twenty-four hours she was back to her old self and the milk was pouring from her. I don't know who was more pleased: me, Roger or Neil.

I got to know Neil quite well over the next few days. He made sure my patient got the best of attention. He fed her and he mucked her out and gave me progress reports whenever I arrived on the farm.

When the day came to take out the stitches Neil wasn't there. Bert, one of the farmhands, helped me instead.

'Young Neil's at the hospital, Mr Taylor.'

'Oh, has there been an accident?'

'No, nothing like that. He's gone for a check up. He goes to Weymouth regular like. You see he's got leukaemia.'

'Is that why he always wears his cap?'

'That's right. But they say his hair will grow again if he gets better.'

I didn't stay long enough in Dorset to know for certain, but as I watched young David Kemp at play with his tractor and his plastic cows I wished with all my heart that Neil did grow up to be a farmer just like his dad.

10

I was in love. Again.

Not that you could blame me. I'd had what you might call a mind-stretching morning with the Krebs cycle. I know Krebs cycle is one of those basic biochemical pathways that everyone needs to know about, but to me it's always looked a bit like a map of the Peking underground. I am not a natural biochemist. The mysteries of the mitochondria will always be just that to me, mysteries.

So, like the rest of my class of second year veterinary students, I was desperate for a coffee and rushed headlong for the refectory as soon as the mighty atom, Ed Dalton, the smallest lecturer in the biochemistry department, had spluttered his final formulae and coughed up his last catalyst.

And there she was. Angela.

'I'm here for my RANA exams,' she replied when Dave Bell asked her why she and her friends had suddenly appeared from nowhere. 'I'm going to be a veterinary nurse.'

They're all called veterinary nurses now, but at the time the best qualification you could get was Registered Animal Nursing Auxiliary, or RANA. Not a very attractive title. In fact the only other auxiliary I knew was the Royal Fleet Auxiliary, which consists mainly of tugboats operating out of Devonport Dockyard. Angela was no tugboat.

She was gorgeous. Long dark hair, and the kind of smile that could reduce a rottweiler to jelly.

'There's a dance tonight, here at the College,' Dave Bell suddenly announced excitedly. 'Perhaps you and some of the other nurses might like to come. You're bound to have a good time.'

Funny isn't it how sometimes you meet someone and you want to impress them with your intelligent conversation and sparkling wit? And yet, somehow, what you come out with makes you look a right twerp.

'I was thinking of having a yoghurt. Can I get you one?'

God, I wish I didn't blush that easily.

I've never found it easy impressing veterinary nurses. And I've tried. Goodness me, I've tried.

Take hamsters. Now, hamsters are the teddy boys of the animal world. Little hardnuts with enough energy to rock 'n' roll all night given a few sunflower seeds. They love to boogie. But not when they're asleep.

Debbie, the veterinary nurse, complained loudly, 'It's no good, there's no way I can get this flipping hamster out of its nest. Every time I go to touch it, it tries to bite me.'

'No problem, leave it to me. I've seen Barbara

Woodhouse blow up a horse's nose. Perhaps I could try that.'

'You can blow up whatever you like. Just get it out of the cage and quick. Mr Lawson will be here in a minute and he wants to see if Hugo's leg is healing.'

I was seeing practice with John Lawson and his partners just outside Truro. They had a great veterinary hospital and lots of veterinary nurses which should have made for a hectic social life. Trouble was they'd seen too many veterinary students come and go. I'd have to work hard to make them take notice of me.

I don't know who told Hugo that hamsters are born athletes, nature's stuntmen, but his favourite trick was to climb the metal bars of his cage and hang there fruitbat-like for a few seconds before taking an Evel Knievel plunge down to his food bowl. You could almost hear him shout 'Geronimo'. It was bound to end in tears. Sure enough when his owner had let him go walkabout on the kitchen table he had taken his chance, raced for the edge, and made his own giant leap for hamsterkind.

That was a couple of weeks before. John Lawson had cleverly made a splint for the fractured right femur out of a piece of old X-ray film and Hugo had taken to his bed to dream of skydives to come. Today John Lawson wanted to see how his patient had been getting on. The trouble was no one could get Hugo out of bed. And bed rest had brought on bad temper.

Amazing how you can do something for a woman which ordinarily you'd never consider. For some men it's parachuting out of helicopters with boxes of milk chocolate. For me it was darting my hand into Hugo's cage and grabbing him by the belly.

I'm told you could hear my scream in Falmouth. The bloody thing bit me. Right through the finger. Big boys and big veterinary students don't cry, they say. Don't you believe it. Ask Debbie.

I met up with Dave Bell and Rob Jones at about eight and we headed up past Euston to Camden Town and the Royal Veterinary College.

'Should be a great night. They've booked some new group I've never heard of. Supertramp or something, but who cares with all those nurses coming along. That Angela's superb. A great night.'

The last time Rob, a farmer's son from South Wales, and I had one of Dave's great nights, it was a night to remember and no mistake. We got arrested and put in the cells at Holborn police station.

'Frisbee, officer . . . we've been playing frisbee,' Rob Jones had explained when the policeman had asked him why we were hurling an old beer tray around the middle of Tavistock Square late that night.

If only he hadn't told him it wasn't our beer tray.

'We got it from the Royal Veterinary College. We went there for a dance, see. We're students.'

'I see sir. You've been helping yourself to college property. You and your fellow frisbee flinger had better come with me.'

Dave Bell was nowhere to be seen. As soon as the police car had turned into the square he'd done a runner and disappeared. Holborn police station wasn't much fun. They took away our green and white college scarves: 'In case you hang yourselves.'

Then we waited for the head barman and the president of the students' union to come and get us released.

As if things weren't bad enough.

Earlier that evening I'd had a stand-up row at the college bar. I'd been shortchanged. I'd given the barman a £10 note and he'd given me the change for a fiver. And now here he was to release me from a police cell. I just hoped he didn't bear a grudge.

The following morning we'd been called before the dean and told our behaviour was more like that of 'Tottenham Hotspur supporters' than future members of a fine and noble profession. If only he knew how often Rob Jones went to see Chelsea.

Yes, Dave Bell's great nights out could be a mixed blessing.

We met Angela and her friends in the bar. Now was my chance. Dave Bell was getting a few drinks. It was now or never.

'Supertramp's not on for a while. There's a bit of a disco first. Do you want a dance?'

I'd put a lot of effort into this. Old Spice aftershave doesn't come cheap and I'd combed my hair to make me look a lot more like Robert Redford – or was it Hank Marvin? – than I usually do. And surely, she couldn't fail to notice my platform shoes and flared jeans. I'd taken the bells off. You can go a little too far in trying to create a sophisticated image, I always think.

Had she forgotten the yoghurt?

'I'd love to,' she said and smiled.

For a moment my heart stopped. I'd never thought of the Royal Veterinary College as anything like paradise, but in that wonderful, wonderful moment, paradise came nowhere close. Together we climbed the stairs to the main hall. You could hardly hear yourself think but I didn't care. Angela and I were going to dance.

I am a lousy dancer. I have no sense of rhythm. Two-step Taylor, Dave Bell had called me. The music starts, I lurch about a bit from side to side. One-two, one-two, till the record ends. I can only dance on autopilot.

Usually these college dances followed a set pattern. 'Brown Sugar' was a big favourite to get the ball rolling. Everyone would be up and about bopping to the Stones. A quick burst of 'Jumping Jack Flash' and I would two-step away with the best of them. Bung on a Rod Stewart, 'Maggie May' or 'You Wear it Well', and you brought the house down. The dance floor would become a heaving sweaty mass with a life of its own. All the vet students were doing exactly what I was doing. Waiting for the slow ones.

If you asked me I'd be hard pressed to choose between 'Albatross' or Harry Nilsson's 'Without You'. Fleetwood Mac are fine but if you want to get really slow and slushy you'd have to go a long way to beat a little touch of Nilsson in the night. I could hardly wait.

I never got that far.

We arrived on the dance floor half way through 'Lola'. Ray Davies was singing his heart out and as we shuffled in the dark I tried my best to make conversation with Angela.

'Where's your practice?' I bellowed.

'Kensington. Mr Samson's.'

I'd heard about Clive Samson's practice. High tech and high powered. He was developing all sorts of wonderful new orthopaedic techniques which even the surgeons at the College hadn't tried yet. Everyone said he had the best-looking nurses in London. If Angela was anything to go by, they were right.

'You enjoy it, then?'

'Oh yes, I love it. Mr Samson's so exciting and he really encourages me with my dancing as well.'

'Dancing?'

'Yes, I've always studied ballet and I'm earning a bit of money now dancing as a go-go girl in some of the West End clubs at night. Mr Samson thinks it's great.'

I bet he did. I was just beginning to realise I was onto a loser when the music started again.

'T Rex. I just adore T Rex.'

As Marc Bolan sang Angela launched into breathtaking action. My bump and grind had seen better days. My twist and shout was tepid. There was no way I was going to fool anybody, never mind the 'children of the revolution'.

Angela was great, though. Suddenly I became aware that everyone else had stopped dancing. Word went down to the bar and Dave Bell and Rob Jones raced to the main hall to see what all the fuss was about. They were very impressed. They cheered as I struggled to increase the pace of my two-step to keep up with Angela's dazzling routine. Eventually it was no good and I just sat on the floor and watched her too.

'You can't win them all,' Dave Bell said as we watched Angela leave with Supertramp, 'not with your feet anyway. I'd knock those platform heels on the head if I was you. They cramp your style.'

I've seen Angela a lot in the years since then. She qualified as a veterinary nurse but it was her dancing that took up most of her life. Wayne Sleep spotted her talent straight away and now she stars with him whenever he puts on a show. Still, a vet can have his memories.

11

'I think Teddy needs a holiday.'

I've always liked collies. Now I know vets aren't meant to have favourites, but I do: border collies and rough collies, I'm soft about them and that's that.

Mind you, it would take a very hard heart not to be soft about Teddy. There are some dogs you know are special. And Teddy is one of them.

'He's in a right state. He's half bald and he won't stop scratching. You don't think it's fleas, do you?' Val Olliver, matron of the hospice, was getting agitated. 'The last thing we need is fleas. He's been down in the dumps like this since his owner, Mrs Crabtree, died.'

Teddy did look pretty miserable, but then if you were up all night playing host to a bunch of fleas using your back as an adventure playground, you'd be pretty miserable too. Funny things, fleas. If you ask me there are a lot more of them about these days. Could be the hole in the ozone layer. A touch of the greenhouse effect turning up the temperature. Fleas love it hot, the hotter the better. After the major epidemic of loft insulation and double glazing all over the country, fleas have never had it so good. The

United Kingdom's become one giant floating flea maternity ward.

It's the cat flea that causes the trouble. Human fleas are now so rare that flea circus owners have almost been forced out of business. You can't train cat fleas and they're too small to be a big hit with the audience. They're very good at making dogs itch and scratch, though. One nibble and sensitive dogs become quaking, quivering heaps. And poor old Teddy was super-sensitive.

'A few good baths in some effective anti-flea shampoo and we'll have his coat growing back in no time,' I reassured Val Olliver. 'It's a flea allergy, but if you spray his bedding and make him wear a flea collar when he's better, he'll be fine. I'll give him an injection to stop him itching.'

It didn't take long for Teddy's coat to grow again. He didn't think much of the baths but he put up with them. Teddy was very good at putting up with things.

'We think he was badly beaten you know, before Mrs Crabtree took him in. He was abandoned when she found him,' Val Olliver told me a few weeks later when Teddy came back to the surgery with a sore eye. 'Of course when she became ill and knew she was dying she had nowhere to go but the hospice, and Teddy came too.'

St Luke's Hospice cares for many terminally ill patients. They're mostly cancer sufferers like Mrs Crabtree. Surprisingly enough it's a very cheerful place; Val Olliver and her dedicated staff wouldn't have it any other way.

'Teddy wouldn't leave her side, Mr Taylor. He really loved Mrs Crabtree and I think it broke his heart when she died.' She told me how the sad black and white collie had spent weeks silently plodding around the hospice. He didn't want to eat and would sit for hours outside the room his owner had died in. 'That's when his coat started falling out. I'm sure it was the grief that did it.'

'Yes,' I said sympathetically. 'He was probably so run down the fleas had a field day. Anyway, he's looking in much better shape now. That eye will soon be better. Conjunctivitis soon responds to treatment. And why don't you get the nurses to give him a few cuddles every now and then? I'm sure that would cheer him up.'

I often prescribe a good cuddle. They don't cost a penny and as far as I know no one's ever complained of any side effects. You can't go wrong with a good cuddle.

It was just what Teddy needed. All the nurses started to make a big fuss of him. And when the patients joined in, the delighted collie was in seventh heaven. He'd never known so much attention.

'You know, I'm sure it makes everyone feel better, just knowing Teddy's there. Sometimes the nights are so very long for some of our patients but he just curls up beside their beds and they feel calm again. They love him.' And I could tell by the way Val Olliver spoke that they weren't the only ones. She had fallen for him too. 'He can stay in the hospice for as long as he wants. I've told him it's against all hospital rules, but what are rules there for if they can't be broken.'

Life in a hospice, like any hospital, can be very busy. Caring's a full time job. The nurses could get some rest and relaxation as between them they worked shifts to cover St Luke's busy days. But Teddy was on call all the time. If anyone was really ill Teddy was there day or night to comfort them. He seemed to have a sixth sense and knew before the doctors who needed special love and attention. When visitors came they took him for long walks up over Jennycliff and along the coast to Bovisand. He would return exhausted and in the middle of the night if anyone called his name he'd be up again and the nurse would find him half asleep comforting the sick and the dying.

All this caring was getting to him. He was worn out.

'A holiday. He needs a holiday,' I'd told Val Olliver when I'd realised how exhausted he was getting. 'A short break will do him the world of good.'

One of the nurses was going down to Cornwall for the week. Teddy went with her. He lay on the beach at St Ives, watched the fishermen landing their catches at Newlyn. In the evenings he'd sit outside the caravan while the nurse and her husband barbecued him a sausage or two. He'd never been happier. On the last night of his holiday the three of them watched the sun go down over St Michael's Mount and Teddy didn't realise it but he'd found himself a new home. Sandra, the nurse, couldn't bear to let him go. There and then as she strolled arm in arm with her husband along the beach, she announced, 'That's it. We're keeping him. He gives out so much love and affection, it's about time he got to keep some for himself. Everyone he loves he loses. But not anymore.'

Teddy still visits St Luke's. In fact he's there almost every day when Sandra goes to work. But when she's off shift Teddy's off shift too. He gets a chance to relax and that has made him healthy and happy.

Not so long ago Jim Sligo, a greyhound breeder, and one of my clients, discoverd he had cancer too. He's been in St Luke's for a few months now.

'Grandad's not been so well,' Sophie Sligo, Jim's little granddaughter, told me the other day when she and her mum brought Holly the guinea pig to the surgery to have her claws clipped. 'Mummy says he's being looked after very well though, so I mustn't worry. I've done a drawing of St Luke's for grandad. Do you want to see it?'

She reached into her coat pocket and pulled out a multicoloured drawing the size of a poster.

'There's grandad. He's in bed.'

'And I suppose that's the nurses and doctors looking after him?'

She nodded and pointed out some more figures which seemed to be hovering above grandad's bed.

'That's the angels. Mummy said the angels are looking after grandad too.'

'And who's that, flying up there with the angels? He doesn't look like an angel to me.' It was Teddy. Sophie had drawn the black and white collie twice as big as any of the other figures. 'He hasn't got any wings.'

'You are silly,' Sophie announced with all the confidence we have at six and wish we could keep for ever. 'Everyone knows you don't need wings to be an angel.'

12

'You can dance to this one.'

Jimmy Bond had to be joking. There was one thing you could guarantee when The Pheasant Pluckers played at the Halfway House: you couldn't move. It was packed.

For a long time Tuesday nights had been a great laugh. If you liked Buddy Holly songs and a bit of fun folk then The Pheasant Pluckers were the group for you. Some nights it seemed half of Plymouth were out to see Jimmy Bond and the rest of the band.

I've always liked Buddy Holly. Ahead of his time and timeless. I used to spend many hours driving to farms around the country lanes of Dartmoor with a tape of Buddy's greatest hits blasting out at full volume.

You won't believe how beautiful a June morning can be until you've seen Dartmoor in early summer. Take the Princetown Road up and out across the moor from Tavistock and you'll see some of the loveliest countryside in Devon. Across to the west is Cornwall and stretching before you as far as you can see in any direction is that marvellous mixture of ancient tors and deep silent valleys, the Dartmoor

National Park. There are often a few ponies and some Galloway cattle grazing on the higher slopes and as I turned off the main road and headed for Peter Tavy they looked up, disturbed by the music roaring from my car. More Buddy Holly fans.

I was heading for Hammerdown farm. Maurice Grubb kept a herd of South Devons there. They were fine cattle with rich yellow red coats. If you wanted good clotted cream you couldn't beat the milk from Maurice's cows. It was a pity Maurice was a miserable old so-and-so but there you are. I had my music and a marvellous Devon morning, I wasn't going to let him get to me.

Hammerdown seemed deserted as I drove into the yard. Maurice had a few cows he wanted me to test to see if they were pregnant and one he thought might be ill with redwater. I've often thought a country vet's job is a bit like being an astronomer: you spend most of your life exploring one black hole after another. It can be a messy business. Looking back on it I spent about five years with a solid yellow brown ring halfway up my right arm. Picasso had his blue period. I had my brown ring period.

Buddy was still giving it stick as I reached into the boot of my car for my calving gown, wellington boots and plastic rectal gloves. 'Oh Boy'. One of my all-time favourites. And, well, you know how it is. Sometimes you just get carried away. 'All of my love, all of my kissing', I sang at the top of my voice as the rock 'n' roll took over, 'You don't know what you've been a-missing. Oh Boy!'

If only I had a guitar. Well, I had the next best thing. A calf puller. You use these in difficult calvings when you haven't got much help. Shaped like a giant T there's a ratchet on them which gives you enough muscle to deliver the biggest of calves. It made a great guitar. Buddy sang. I played. What the row of South Devon cows waiting beside the cattle crush, or the two farm collies, thought of this rural rocker in a green overall and wellington boots I'll never know. They watched as I danced and bopped around the farmyard, lost in a world of my own. The chickens and the geese enjoyed it, joining in with loud raucous squawks. 'The world will see, that you were meant for me!' I finished with a flourish. The chickens went bananas and the collies barked furiously.

'Right, that's it then. The bloody cabaret's over. You've got work to do.' Maurice Grubb had appeared in the barn doorway. He'd seen the whole perform-ance. He was almost smiling.

I fumbled around trying to decide if his cows were pregnant. Most were, one or two weren't. I've always found I do this sort of work best if I keep my eyes tightly closed. In the early stages a pregnant uterus slips and slides around and isn't easy to feel. You need all the concentration you can get. Anyway, if I kept my eyes tightly shut I wouldn't have to look at Maurice's smirking face. I'd never seen him so happy. He wasn't going to let me forget today.

'This heifer's got redwater, I'm sure of it,' Maurice informed me. 'She's pretty dull and look at that, every time she passes water it's as red as hell.'

We see a lot of redwater in Devon and Cornwall. It's caused by a protozoan parasite, Babesia, which cows pick up from ticks that latch onto them while they're out grazing the fields. The sheep tick Ixodes ricinus is the culprit. There's always loads of them around in May and June when the temperatures start to rise. Ticks are great survivors. I see lots of dogs and cats with them today in my Plympton practice even though it's been years since anyone kept sheep anywhere near. When they built all the new houses, no one told the ticks so they wait in the long grass for a passing ewe or ram. It's a bit like waiting for a bus. If you can't get a sheep, then it's any port in a storm, and the first dog or cat that hurries by will do.

'She'll need some Diampron. That'll kill the Babesia,' I explained to Maurice. 'Let's hope not too many of her red blood cells are damaged before she starts to get better.' The protozoa attack the red blood cells causing haemolysis. In no time at all the cow's urine turns bright red. That's what gives the disease its name and makes it easy for farmers like Maurice to spot. 'Her temperature's very high at the moment. I'll come back in a day or two to see how she's getting on.'

'Thanks,' said Maurice with a smirk. 'And bring your guitar next time. Your calf puller was out of tune.'

I came back the following day. The heifer, Hazel by name, seemed a bit brighter. Her temperature had come down and her urine was getting clearer. The

Diampron seemed to be working. Using Diampron was a bit of an art. You had to give enough to deal with the infection but not so much as to kill all the babesia in the cow's body. Leaving some protozoa circulating gave the cow a degree of future immunity.

The next day Maurice Grubb was getting worried.

'She's not passing red water any more, but God she looks ill. You'd better come quick.'

I raced up to Hammerdown. Hazel was in a bad way. Her condition had suddenly deteriorated. She was very thin and seemed to be dehydrated. She just lay there in the barn uninterested in anything. The babesia had done more .damage to her blood cells than I had realised. If we didn't do something quick she would die.

'She needs a blood transfusion. Now.'

'I didn't know you could give cows a blood transfusion. Are you sure it is going to work?'

I wasn't sure but it was all we could do. The practice saw about four hundred cases of redwater a year. Usually only four or five would need blood transfusions but you could never be sure. Hazel was the first this year.

'We'll need a donor. Preferably a cow who isn't pregnant. One of those we examined a couple of days ago will do.'

'I'll go and fetch Ruth. She's six years old and has always seemed fine. We'll use her.'

Maurice herded Ruth into the barn and I got ready to collect some blood. 'I'll need to cut into her jugular vein. I use a large needle to draw the blood out. Some local anaesthetic will stop her feeling it too much.'

Ruth stood there patiently as I injected a bleb of local anaesthetic under her skin. Then gently I inserted the large collection needle into the vein. Dark red blood flowed freely.

'We need about five litres. We'll run them into these dialysis bags we got from Tavistock Hospital. There's some citrate and some dextrose in them which will stop the blood from clotting.'

'Don't you have to worry about blood groups?'

'No,' I replied. 'I usually leave that sort of thing to Tony Hancock. You're usually safe if you're only going to transfuse a cow once or twice. There's not much known about cattle blood groups. We'll just have to take a chance.'

Once the blood was collected I took the dialysis bags over beside Hazel and started the transfusion.

'We'll use her jugular vein too. I'll run the blood in slowly and we'll see if she improves.'

If you have to give a blood transfusion to a cow you have to give it at the right time. Give it too early while the babesia are active and you'll just be giving them an extra meal of red blood cells. I had to hope the Diampron had killed most of them.

It took about forty-five minutes to give Hazel her transfusion. It seemed to perk her up almost straight away. Maurice Grubb was delighted. Perhaps he wasn't so miserable as I'd been led to believe.

'Does Ruth here get a badge, now she's a blood

donor like?' he asked me as I sewed up the cut I had made over her jugular vein.

'Sorry, Mr Grubb. I haven't even got any tea and biscuits for her. But I'm sure you'll find her some extra hay.'

Hazel soon got better. It was a bad year for redwater and before long I seemed to be doing blood transfusions all over the place. The great thing was that most of the cows recovered.

A few weeks later I was having a pint in the Halfway House. Jimmy Bond and the Pheasant Pluckers were in full swing with 'Raining in my heart' when Dave Bryant, Maurice Grubb's neighbour came over to me.

'I met old misery guts in Tavistock market the other day. Seems you've made him a happy man. Curing his cow and something about giving him the best laugh he's had in a long time. He said if I saw you I was to give you a message.'

'Oh yes, and what's that?' I replied.

Dave Bryant grinned and nudged me with his elbow in the ribs. 'Buddy Holly lives!'

13

Me and Barney, we have a game. It's called tear up the record card. It works like this. I arrive at Barney's house in Mannamead and ring the bell. Mrs Harvey, Barney's mum, opens the door and lets me in. I take a seat and open up my medical bag. One glimpse of his case history and Barney makes a dive for it. We then spend the rest of the visit tussling for it at regular intervals. Barney always wins. The card's a bit tatty and held together by sellotape. It's full of tooth holes and you can hardly read a thing.

'Mr Taylor, you probably won't remember me, but about ten years ago you saved my dog Barney's life.' Mrs Harvey was almost in tears as she spoke to me. 'He's nearly fourteen now and he can hardly breathe. I've always had a lot of faith in you but I didn't realise you'd come back home to practise in Plymouth. Can you help him?'

I drove to Barney's house as fast as I could. The traffic at Marsh Mills was as horrendous as ever and I began to wonder if I'd get there in time.

'He's had a heart attack. But that's not all. I'm pretty sure he's had emphysema for a long while. It'll be touch and go.' I injected Barney with a heart stimulant and gave him a diuretic and a steroid to help his breathing. If I was lucky he would start to recover soon.

'You saved his life you know. He was ever so ill back then. Parvovirus, you said. All those poor dogs really sick.' Mrs Harvey continued, 'You said you'd never ever seen it before.'

When the dogs started dying I began to wonder why I'd ever bothered to become a vet at all. It was the saddest job of all.

I was working in a big, busy veterinary hospital and none of us had ever seen anything like it. The first cases were seen up around London. Whole litters of young puppies were just giving up and dying. Their hearts were weakened and they had the most awful diarrhoea and vomiting. Older dogs were no better off. The virus attacked them without warning and within hours they were desperately ill. Most went into shock with severe dehydration caused by the terrible bloody gastroenteritis that affected them.

All over the world the same sad story was repeating itself. Vets didn't have a clue where it came from or what it was. A new virus had arrived to attack the world's dogs who had no protection against it. It was so new that although I was just out of college I was no better informed than vets who had been in practice for twenty years. It was too new for the textbooks and the veterinary schools were only just now starting to research and understand it.

The first words Mrs Harvey ever spoke to me were,

'This is Barney and he's ever so ill. He can't stop being sick. I think he's dying.'

The young labrador looked in a bad way. His temperature was soaring. His eyes were sunken and his skin was pinched tight to the touch. He was badly dehydrated. And the smell. God, the smell. A haemorrhagic gastroenteritis. Terrible.

'Is he the sort of chap who swallows things?' I asked. There was just a chance Barney might have a foreign body tucked away inside him causing his digestive upset.

'He used to go for stones and things when he was younger. But no, not recently I'm sure.' Mrs Harvey paused and started to cry. 'Is he going to die?'

'I'll do what I can, but I can't promise. Let's see if we can get through tonight and we'll go from there.'

Sandra and Judy, the nurses, carried Barney gently through to the ward. There were dogs everywhere.

'We'll have to put him on a drip. It's our only chance,' I said.

The girls were getting to be expert at intravenous fluids. I don't think any of us had ever set up so many drips. Antibiotics were pretty useless in the face of the infection. They might help to bring the sick dogs' temperatures down but they were pretty useless against the virus itself. The only chance you had was to stop the poor things from becoming too dehydrated. This was why the intravenous fluids were so important.

'Raise Barney's vein if you can. I'll see if I can thread an indwelling catheter into it.' Sandra cuddled the weary Labrador and gently pressed her thumb across the top of his foreleg. His vein rose. It wasn't brilliant but it would have to do.

'Got it. Thank God for that. Now we can run the lactated Ringer's solution into him as fast as we dare. You stay with him. I'll check on the others.'

Sam the collie seemed beyond hope. His drip was still in place but his breathing was becoming more and more shallow as I watched. His mucous membranes were so very, very pale. He didn't stand a chance.

I was getting tired. The days were ever so busy but the nights, those long parvo nights, were the worse. I hated losing all these lovely animals and feeling so useless. Caesar the German Shepherd was failing too. He could just about manage a feeble wag of his tail as I patted him but it was hopeless. We were losing him. Lucy the lovely little Cavalier King Charles couldn't stop being sick. She looked forlorn and puzzled as every few minutes she retched and retched. I just wanted to cry. Gordon, the once magnificent Great Dane was the first to die that night. Judy called me over urgently as the huge dog went into one final, painful spasm.

'Nigel, I can't bear to watch,' she cried. 'I thought he'd started to improve. Poor Gordon.'

'I'd better phone his owners. I bloody hate this job,' I said as I picked up the telephone that hung from the ward wall.

'I'm sorry, Mrs Wyatt. I'm afraid Gordon has died.'

There was a pause as Mrs Wyatt took in the awful news. 'But he was only two, Mr Taylor. I'd had him vaccinated against distemper and everything. It seems so unfair. Isn't there a vaccine you can use to protect dogs against this virus? He didn't suffer, did he?'

What could I say?

'One day, Mrs Wyatt. One day there'll be vaccines I'm sure. But right now there aren't any. Some vets are starting to use cat vaccines, meant to protect against feline enteritis, to protect dogs. I'm sure we'll do the same but once a dog shows signs of parvovirus most die. I'm ever so sorry.'

As the night drew on I sat with Barney for hours just holding his paw and talking to him as the nurses went about their work. Funny the things you tell them when they're very ill. They don't ask us for much so you tell them how much they're loved and how they'll enjoy all those lovely walks when they're better again. I'm soft about dogs. I hope I never change. I lost count of the number of cups of coffee I drank that night to keep myself awake.

Even so I think I must have fallen asleep just before dawn. I was woken by the sound of tearing. It was Barney. He was sitting up and wagging his tail. He must have grabbed his record card from my hand while I was asleep. He was ripping it to pieces.

'Barney, you big chump. You've made it.'

That was over ten years ago now. Today there are marvellous vaccines that prevent parvovirus being the terrible scourge it was back then. Sometimes I talk to younger vets and I tell them about the night all the dogs died. They've never seen anything like it. I hope they never do. And the strange thing is that there are still loads of dog owners who never have their dogs vaccinated at all and loads more I'm sure who don't think that small amount of coloured liquid we inject into a dog's neck does any good at all. If only they could have been with me that night and seen what I saw.

Barney doesn't know it, but if he hadn't lived I would probably have given up being a vet altogether. I couldn't bear to see any more animals die.

Every month now I go and visit him. I give him a check-up. His heart's better and his emphysema's easier. It's his birthday soon. Fifteen. Hard to imagine as I see the old boy charge around the front room that once I never thought he'd make it to the morning.

I'm told that there are certain sounds that make your spine tingle. Pavarotti in the Park, Carreras at Covent Garden. But for me nothing could ever compare with the sound of ripping paper . . . Barney tearing up his record card.

14

'And how long did you say you've been sleeping with your iguana?'

This was more like it. Almost like being a proper vet. The Beaumont Animal Hospital. A real posers' palace for every third and fourth year veterinary student who'd made it through the hard grind of pre-clinical studies. You could start forgetting most of the academic theory they'd spent the past few years ramming into you. Now the proper work began. You had to learn the art of clinical veterinary medicine which as far as I could see meant wearing a white coat, dangling a stethoscope round your neck and combing your hair a little more often than usual.

When one of the Beaumonts, a Mrs Grove-Grady, died back in the twenties she had this great idea to use the bulk of her estate to set up a sort of modern Noah's Ark in the middle of Salisbury Plain. Naturally enough the British army which spends most of its time there on manoeuvres with tanks and other toys weren't too keen on sharing their ranges with rampant reindeer or the odd rhino, so Noah's Ark mark two was a bit of a non-starter. In those days the Royal Veterinary College wasn't much better than a slum.

The buildings were delapidated and falling down but soon the whole place was going to be rebuilt. So the Beaumonts' cash came to Camden Town and the Beaumont Hospital was built. It's been busy ever since.

'I've got just the case for you,' Alexander Gordon-Brown, former London Zoo vet and now Professor of Medicine informed us as we piled into his office on our first day running the Beaumont's clinics. 'It's an iguana from Ilford.'

I could be wrong but I always thought iguanas came from somewhere vaguely exotic like South America or the Galapagos Islands. That's where David Attenborough always seemed to be bumping into them. I'd never seen '*Zoo Quest* goes to Ilford'. Mind you, no one was going to argue with AG-B. If AG-B said the iguana came from Ilford, then Ilford it was.

'Mavis has been ill for a while. I've got to give a lecture on panda fertility to the final year so I'll be away for an hour or two. Perhaps, Mr Taylor and Mr Richmond, you'd be so kind as to get a full clinical history from Mavis's owners and perform any diagnostic tests you think necessary.'

AG-B was a great panda man. He'd travelled all over the world as they tried unsuccessfully to mate London Zoo's Chi-Chi. Trouble was she was in love with her keeper. After all, she'd never seen another panda until An-An was rudely thrust upon her. If only someone had bought An-An a keeper's cap, it would have been all the romance Chi-Chi needed.

'How many iguanas you examined, Nigel?' Graham Richmond asked me as we walked along to the consulting room where Mavis and her mum and dad were waiting for us.

'About as many as you. So I guess I'm pretty expert.'

'This is your first, then,' Graham replied with a grin. 'You've got to start somewhere. Can't stay an innocent all your life.'

We introduced ourselves to Mr and Mrs Dingle. 'This is Mr Richmond,' I said confidently. 'He has a special interest in lizards. Where's Mavis?'

'In there,' said Mr Dingle, pointing to a large holdall on the consulting table with 'Help The Aged' written in big blue letters across it. It was wriggling ominously. 'She's having one of her tantrums. We had to come here by tube. Mavis doesn't like the tube.'

Mr Dingle unzipped the holdall and the large dark green lizard was revealed. She was massive. I couldn't be sure but I'd swear she was nearly five or six foot long. You'd have thought to look at her that she came from the land that time forgot, never mind Ilford.

'So she's not well,' I ventured as Graham started to listen to her chest with a stethoscope. What he could hear was anybody's guess as she was hissing like a pressure cooker about to blow. 'Perhaps you'd tell us a little bit about her.'

'I found her in a pet shop in Ilford,' said Mr Dingle. 'All alone she was and I felt ever so sorry for her. So I went in and bought her and took her home there and then.'

'I wasn't too amused at the time,' Mrs Dingle, who looked a lot like Jane Seymour and whom Graham and I had already decided could be of a lot more interest than Mavis, continued. 'But I soon grew to love her. Hubby and I we've each given her our own hot water bottle to keep her warm. Mavis likes the heat, you know.' Graham and I nodded. From the holdall she pulled two hot water bottles. Pink and blue. His and Hers.

'Just the job,' Graham observed authoritatively.

Mr Dingle went on to tell us how he'd become devoted – no, obsessed – with Mavis and her health. He'd bought all the books there were on iguanas and knew everything there was to know about them. He'd even given up his job to look after her when she became unwell.

Iguanas are poikilotherms. That means they're more active when they're hot. I'm much the same in reverse. All day Mavis would parade leisurely around Mr Dingle's heated flat. The trouble was she wouldn't go to sleep unless he turned the heating down and the lights off. First thing in the morning as the sun crept up over the roofs of Ilford she would stir and angrily demand the heating's return.

'How do you know when she's angry?' I asked, looking at the serene dragon as she lay on the consulting table.

'Easy, really,' answered Mr Dingle. 'She turns black and jumps for me throat.'

'Of course,' I said knowledgeably. 'Wonderfully demonstrative pets, iguanas, aren't they?'

'I think she's got rickets,' Mr Dingle informed us as we finished our examination and note taking.

'Could be, could be,' said Graham slowly and deliberately. Dingle was probably right. Most of these exotic pets never get the right mix of minerals and vitamins in their diet. Owners did their best but Ilford, or anywhere else in Britain, isn't much of a substitute for the Galapagos with its sunshine and natural iguana food. 'We'll have to take some X-rays to be sure. But that's no real problem.'

Oh yes it was.

The duty radiographer didn't like Mavis. 'I'm not going anywhere near that. The last time I saw anything like that it was trying to eat Racquel Welch.' Now that wasn't such a bad idea but I knew what she meant. It's a bit like rats and mice. You either like lizards or you don't. 'Anyway, she won't stay still enough to X-ray. She'll have to be anaesthetised.'

'I've heard you can stick them in the fridge. They go really quiet then,' Graham suggested.

'I bet they do. You would, too. No, we'd better get one of the anaesthetists to have a look.'

It took a while. Most veterinary anaesthetists think nothing of sending a dog or cat off to sleep, but iguanas? First you had to find a text book.

'Says here ketamine's worth a try,' Andy Compton, the Beaumont's houseman, informed us. 'We'll give it a whirl.'

It worked a treat. Mavis stayed as still as could be

for her X-ray. The radiographer still stood on a chair and looked the other way as she pressed the exposure button on the machine, though. There's just no pleasing some people.

'It's rickets,' we informed the Dingles. 'See how her bones are bent and swollen? Mr Gordon-Brown will be back soon and once he's seen our report and looked at these X-rays he'll tell you how you can improve Mavis's diet.'

'Is it going to take long for her to get well?' Mrs Dingle asked us anxiously. 'I'm not one to complain, but lately since she's been ill my husband will insist she sleeps in our bed to keep warm. I've told him I'm staying on the sofa till she's better. You've got no idea what it's like trying to get a decent night's sleep with an iguana in the bed.'

Graham and I looked at each other bemused. This was one for Claire Rayner, not us. Lovely Mrs Dingle on the sofa while Mr D. snuggled up with the creature from the black lagoon?

'I wonder how she's getting on?' Graham asked idly as we went into the lab for our Thursday afternoon pathology practical a week or so later.

'Who? Mrs Dingle?'

'No, you chump. Mavis. They loved that lizard, you know. Just like lots of people love their Jack Russells or their moggies.'

'I know,' I said compassionately. 'But I've got a feeling Mavis hasn't got on too well.'

I gave him the tiny specimen pot that was lying on the bench in front of us. The label told its own story. Not the sort of thing you see every day in Camden Town. *'Iguana Pancreas'*.

15

I'm sure the girl behind the counter at Woolworth's didn't have a clue what I was up to. One moment I was poking about the pick-'n'-mix looking for my favourite toffee whirls, the next I was jumping about, punching the air with my fist and whooping for joy as if I'd just won the pools.

Only it was better than that. I'd suddenly realised that Lucky Smith was alive and well. She was going to make it.

I know I'll never be another Christiaan Barnard or Maghdi Yacoub, but a vet can dream, can't he? Even the world's best transplant surgeons must start somewhere. I wonder what it must be like operating with a dedicated team of highly skilled surgeons, anaesthetists and nurses in a marvellous operating theatre filled with every latest gadget and gismo medical science can come up with. Usually it's just Louise and me and a Fluotec Mark 3. Not what you might call high tech but we do our best.

Mrs Smith had spoken to me on the phone late at night, almost in tears. 'It's Lucky. She's been hit by a car. Can I bring her to you straight away?'

Someday someone will bring out a highway code

for cats and perhaps they'll read it, but until then I suppose vets will always be kept busy putting them back together again.

'The car went right over her. My neighbour saw it happen. She's having a lot of trouble breathing.'

The tiny black and white cat was certainly struggling. Every breath seemed to be an effort. She was bleeding from her mouth but amazingly no bones seemed to be broken. When I listened to her chest, I could hardly hear her heart at all, there was so much fluid about.

'I'm sure she's got some pretty severe internal injuries. I'll give her some injections for the pain and the shock,' I told her worried owner. 'An intravenous drip will help get her over the shock. Then we'll have to wait and see.'

'Is she going to live? The kids think the world of her. I don't want to lose her,' Mrs Smith sobbed.

'I'll do what I can. No promises. First we'll get her through the night and tomorrow we'll perhaps X-ray her to find out what's happened inside.'

Lucky hung on to life that night. Cats are great survivors. Perhaps that's why everybody seems to think they have nine lives. They can bounce back from the most appalling injuries. Next morning she was a bit brighter but still not well enough to X-ray. Her breathing was starting to settle but it still wasn't quite right.

'She's got a ruptured diaphragm,' I told Mrs Smith a day or so later when her condition had improved enough for me to X-ray her. 'We'll have to operate and repair it or she'll be in real trouble.' The diaphragm divides the chest from the abdomen. It's mainly muscle, so it's very strong and usually quite hard to damage. Getting squashed by a car, though, is a pretty good way of tearing a hole in it.

Sometimes these tears can be very tiny and it may take a few weeks for the damage to cause any discomfort. Not so long ago, one Christmas Day, I was called out in the early hours by a Cornish family who were visiting their friends in Plympton for the holiday. They had two lovely German Shepherds, Bruce and Sabre. About six weeks earlier Sabre had been hit by a car near Penzance.

He'd been taken to one of the local vets who told his owner he was shaken up but seemed to have had a lucky escape. In fact he'd torn his diaphragm. Just a little tear, sitting there waiting to cause trouble. On Christmas Eve they'd taken the two of them up onto the moors up by Cadover bridge. The dogs loved it and were having a great rough and tumble when Sabre suddenly squealed out in pain. They took him home and he improved as the evening went on. About midnight he started to have terrible difficulty breathing and they brought him to me. He died on the consulting table before I could do anything. The small tear had suddenly got much bigger as he played with Bruce. His liver and intestines plunged forward into his chest and there was nothing I could do to save him.

I showed Lucky's X-ray to Louise, my nurse. 'Look, you can hardly see Lucky's heart. All that intestine lying over the top of it. Her lungs are so badly compressed it's a wonder she can breathe at all.' We wouldn't have long once Lucky was anaesthetised. It was important Louise knew what she was doing.

'Once I've injected her with anaesthetic I'll tube her as quick as I can. I'll spray some local on her larynx to stop her gagging when I put the endotracheal tube in.' Cats have got really sensitive throats. Lucky needed a tube down her trachea to breathe with, but putting it there had to be done with a lot of care.

'Bingo. Got it in one,' I cried as the tube slid easily into position. 'We'll keep her under with as little halothane as possible, just in case.'

There was a big hole connecting the abdomen and the chest. So once I made my first incision, Louise would have to take over Lucky's breathing for her. No high-tech equipment here, just a rubber bag being squeezed rhythmically minute after minute for as long as it takes.

'Good, Louise. I can see her lungs puffing up and down through this hole in her diaphragm. Her heart's beating well, too.'

Gently I eased back all the intestine I could find in the chest. As I did so you could see her lungs get even pinker, free at last of the awful pressure that the bowel had been putting on them.

'I'll sew the diaphragm up with some Dexon. If I'm lucky it'll hold and the chest will be sealed again.'

The trick is to put your last stitch in just as your assistant inflates the lungs. That way you avoid as far as possible leaving too much air in the chest, which can cause a pneumothorax.

'Now,' I cried at Louise as I got ready to put the last stitch in place. 'Keep breathing for her whilst I sew up her belly.'

I worked as quickly as I could. I could start to relax a bit now. The worst of the operation was over but we still had to wait to see if she could breathe for herself once Louise stopped 'bagging' her.

'Fingers crossed. Here goes.'

Louise stopped the rhythmic squeezing of the black anaesthetic bag. It was an anxious few moments. At first there was nothing, and I began to despair.

'Come on, *come on*,' I muttered.

Then with a wonderful, deep, deliberate breath the tiny cat started to breathe for herself. It was marvellous.

'She's there, Louise. She's bloody well there.'

We watched as the cat's breathing became ever more regular and relaxed. The colour came flooding back into her gums and when I listened to her chest with a stethoscope I could hear her heart beating louder and clearer than ever before.

'We'll give her some antibiotics and then we'll just have to wait and see. Twenty-four hours and we'll know for sure.'

I'm always amazed at how quickly animals get over their operations. You and me, we'd be in bed for weeks moaning at the nurses and getting sick of grapes. But animals are different. They just get on with it. Her stitches didn't bother her at all and as each day went by you could see her getting stronger and stronger. In fact she never looked back.

'I'll give her a cuddle before she goes. I'm really going to miss her,' Louise told me the morning the Smiths came to take her home.

They filled the consulting room and the children chattered away delightedly as the young cat purred its head off.

'I nearly forgot, Mr Taylor,' Mrs Smith said as she reached into her handbag. 'I thought you might like these.' It was a packet of toffee whirls.

'My favourite.'

'I know. My sister-in-law Sharon works in Woolworth's selling sweets.'

I started to blush, remembering the pick-'n'-mix.

'She says you go really nuts over toffee whirls.'

16

Cameron Scott, they said, ran one of the best practices on Dartmoor. He enjoyed having veterinary students come to work with him but he wasn't easily impressed with academic niceties. Exams didn't matter half as much as how you grappled with galloping Galloways or held on to heavy horses' hooves. If he liked you, you had a great time and learnt a lot. If he didn't, then he could be like the moor itself. Tough, hard and unforgiving.

'We've got a busy day ahead of us, laddie,' he had announced that morning when I arrived at his Tavistock surgery. 'I hope you're not like the last student I had. Useless is too good a word for him. You should see the dent he left in my car.'

Cameron had been castrating a colt high on the moor near Two Bridges. In the old days vets used to do this with the horse standing. You'd nip under its belly and poke around its testicles with a syringe loaded with local anaesthetic. Not the sort of job for the faint-hearted. I wouldn't attempt it, even with a crash helmet! Some vets still do standing castrations but most, like Cameron that day on Dartmoor, prefer their patients to have a general anaesthetic and sleep like babies through the whole thing. Cameron liked to use an intravenous anaesthetic which had the advantage of an antidote you could give once the operation was over so the horse would quickly recover.

The castration itself was fairly uneventful, although I'm sure if asked, the young colt wouldn't have been too pleased. He'd staggered about a bit when Cameron gave him the anaesthetic injection and then crashed to the soft moorland turf immobilised and ready for surgery. Cameron swiftly got on with the job in hand. Once the castration was complete he quickly injected the antidote into the horse's jugular vein and waited for him to recover.

'If I were you I'd move your car, Mr Scott,' Brian Murray, a final-year student from Bristol vet school, had told him. 'I've seen a few of these chaps come round at college. They can be very unpredictable you know, and your car's a bit close to him.'

Cameron liked to drive his car right into the middle of the field when he was operating. That way he had all his instruments and his medicines just there ready to be used.

'I've never had a problem laddie. Give the horse a tetanus shot. The car stays where it is.'

As if on cue the colt, which had been taking its time coming round, suddenly recovered and shot to its feet. It was up but pretty unsteady. It wobbled backwards, forwards and then with a mighty crash stumbled sideways and came to rest sitting contentedly on Cameron's bonnet before with one final lurch it slid back to the ground.

'Bloody students!' Cameron exclaimed before word-
lessly he loaded up his car and headed back to
Tavistock leaving Brian to hitch a lift home from a
passing ice cream van.

And now it was my turn.

'We've got some calves to disbud at Toby Dawe's
farm. I'll show you how to do the first one, laddie,
and then you can do the rest.'

There were ten young Friesian calves waiting in
Toby's barn. Most had tiny buds where the horns
would grow if left but one or two were a bit older and
their young horns seemed a little more substantial.

'You put the local in just here behind the eye. That
way it blocks the nerve supply to the horn and they
don't feel a thing,' Cameron said as we caught the
first calf. 'Then you can burn off the horn with this
disbudding iron. Those bigger ones you'll have to saw
through first before you use the iron.'

And that was it. End of lesson. From then for the
next half hour I got on with the veterinary side of
things whilst Cameron, cigarette in mouth, sat on a
nearby bale and read the *Financial Times*.

'Not too bad, laddie. A bit more speed next time
and you'll be fine,' he told me as I stood, sweat
pouring off me, recovering from wrestling with the
calves and the hot iron. 'Not as easy as it looks, is it?'

We drove over the moor to Merrivale. Trevor Able
had some bullocks that needed castrating.

'Bloody hell. they're enormous,' I exclaimed as I
saw the size of the Galloways we had to see to. 'I

thought you only castrated calves when they were young.'

'Anything up to a year old is young enough for some of our moorland farmers, laddie,' Cameron informed me. 'Don't worry. After the first kick you won't notice a thing.'

Trevor Able and his son herded them as best they could one by one into the makeshift crush they'd rigged up out of a swinging gate which you could press tight against a crumbling moorland wall. It didn't look too safe to me.

'There you are, laddie. A pair of Burdizzos, off you go.' Burdizzos are like giant pincers. The trick is to place them accurately over the spermatic cord and close them tight across it cutting off the blood supply to each testicle in turn. They're cleverly designed so that they don't cut the skin, only the artery and vein beneath. They're not the easiest of things to use even if your patient is playing the game and standing still. These Galloways were having none of it. They'd jiggle frantically up and down while I tried to manoeuvre the Burdizzos in place. Then there'd be an awesome bellow as I squeezed it tight, followed by two cloven hooves narrowly missing my nose.

'I see British Steel is not what it was,' Cameron calmly observed as another Galloway hollered in disgust. 'Good job our money's in oil, isn't it, Trevor?'

Castrating those Galloways seemed to take ages and when Cameron suggested a pint at the Leaping Salmon, I couldn't wait.

'We've got to pop next door first,' he said as we

arrived in Horrabridge. 'Old Mrs Endacott has got a very sick dachshund I think we'll have to put to sleep.'

Trudy the dachshund wasn't at all well. Nearly fifteen, she'd suddenly lost all her weight and it was pretty obvious her kidneys were failing. She didn't really have a future.

'My young colleague Mr Taylor here will gently give her an injection, Mrs Endacott. Trudy won't know a thing.'

'I've hardly ever done this,' I whispered anxiously. 'What if I miss the vein?'

'You won't, laddie, you won't. Just get on with it.'

I drew the pentobarbitone into the syringe while Cameron cradled the tiny dog in his arms. I clipped some hair away from her foreleg and dabbed it with surgical spirit. Cameron raised the vein by putting his thumb across it at the elbow. His eyes were tightly closed.

'There,' I said. 'In first time. She didn't know it was happening.'

I was relieved. Dachshund veins aren't the easiest of things to find. Tiny little legs that bend all over the place. No wonder Cameron had kept his eyes shut. I bet he thought I was going to miss.

Over lunch in the Leaping Salmon, Cameron discussed the price of cocoa and sugar futures with Ray the landlord. I hadn't realised the FT 100 was such an essential part of veterinary medicine. But they'd told me seeing practice with Cameron was an education. It was. It would have been great if you were going to be a stockbroker, never mind a stock tender.

As we drove back along the Tavistock road, Cameron's radio crackled into life.

'Terry Sweet's got an emergency. One of his Jersey cows has been hit by a tractor. Can you go there straight away?'

We roared along the country lanes at high speed. Terry Sweet's farm was over at Buckland Monachorum, normally about twenty minutes' drive. We were there in less than ten.

'She's in a bad way, Cameron. One of my young lads was bringing the silage in from the fields. Someone must have left a gate open.' Terry Sweet loved his Jersey cows. Seeing one like this was breaking his heart. 'I'm sure you'll have to shoot her.'

Cameron swiftly examined her. One of her back legs was badly broken and you could see the white of the bone jutting out through the torn skin.

'Yes Terry,' he said resignedly. 'She doesn't have a hope. We'll shoot her straight away.'

Cameron reached for the Webley pistol he always carried in his car, loaded it and came over to me. He handed me the gun. 'There, laddie. I'll show you where to place the gun and you can fire it.'

Cameron ordered everyone back out of the way and then took a step back as I took aim with the pistol pressed close to the cow's head.

There was a loud crack which deafened me for a moment and with one great convulsion the injured cow fell dead.

'Good man,' Cameron said as we drove off to our next call. 'This next job's not so bad. We've got to stitch up a Dartmoor pony that got caught in some barbed wire yesterday.'

It was a long drive to Spriddlescombe farm. Cameron didn't mention a thing about Terry Sweet's cow. I'd never shot anything before and the whole episode had really upset me. For a long time he was silent and then he started to ask me what I knew of stocks and shares and the equity market.

'Not a lot,' I said resignedly, 'but then it's kind of hard to play the stock market on a student grant. One day maybe, but right now I find it hard enough keeping myself going with beer and Mars Bars.'

Bill Wotton's pony wasn't too badly injured. She had a nasty gash in the side of her chest which would have to be cleaned up and sutured. Cameron showed me how to put the local anaesthetic in just the right places so she wouldn't feel it and then sat back with his head buried in his *Financial Times* as I stitched away.

'Always the same. Doesn't ever change,' Bill Wotton confided in me as we crouched over the pony's wound. 'I expect he's got you to do everything today. 'Course he'll operate if he has to, but if he's got a student he can trust he'll sit back with his stocks and shares and let them get on with it.'

'That's right,' I said. 'He's kept me pretty busy.'

''Course he has,' Bill replied. 'Likes to give the impression he's hard as nails. But I'll tell you this: there's no one likes seeing animals suffer less than Mr Scott. That's why he doesn't like doing anything to them that might hurt them.'

I looked across at the burly figure in the corner of the farmyard flicking through the pink pages of his favourite newspaper, and thought back over the day. Terry Sweet's Jersey cow, Trudy the dachshund and all those grunting Galloways and Friesian calves. No wonder I'd been busy doing the hard man's work.

That's why all he talked about was stocks and shares. He didn't want me to even guess at his true feelings. But now I knew for sure.

Cameron Scott was soft.

17

'Do you believe in ghosts?'

Mrs Sutton had brought her new kitten Tuppence
to see me. 'Only, it's Arthur. He hasn't gone away
you know. I still hear him purring and miaowing
around the house. And he won't let Tuppence rest.
Whenever I put food down for her I hear him growl
and she gets frightened. I'm going to have to get him
exorcized.'

I'd put poor old Arthur to sleep about two months
before. He was a lovely Burmese cat. Like a lot of
older cats he'd been fine until his kidneys started to
deteriorate. Then he just gradually got thinner and
thinner until there was nothing left of him. I often
think old cats are a bit like old soldiers. They don't
die, they just fade away. Trouble was, Arthur hadn't
faded away enough. I knew he'd always loved Mrs
Sutton and the fuss she'd made of him. Perhaps he
didn't want to let her go.

I must admit I'm not a great fan of the dark. And
that's no joke if you're a country vet. When you're out
late at night travelling to some remote moorland farm
it's amazing how you suddenly believe all those stories

you've heard about headless huntsmen and hairy hands that suddenly reach in and drive you off the road. I just turn up Radio 2 as loud as I can and keep whistling when it gets really spooky.

The mist was making it impossible to see more than a foot or two in front of me as I drove along the pitted moorland track to Trowlesworthy farm that night. Peter Norman had a cow calving. Molly, a favourite Friesian.

As I drove into Trowlesworthy I could see a lonely figure swinging a flickering hurricane lamp. 'She's in the yard. You can help me put her in the barn.' It was Terry, Peter's young farmhand. 'Mr Norman's gone to bed. He says you and me can cope with Molly.'

'Sounds fine to me. Let's go for it.'

I always carry a halter in the back of the car. I slipped it over her head and with a little gentle persuasion Terry and I led her into the barn.

That's when our troubles started. Normally calving cows just stand around fairly uninterested while you do your obstetrical best sorting out the jumble of tangled limbs you usually find inside. But Molly was having none of it. She bellowed loudly and barged Terry and me out the way as she headed for the open door behind us. There was no way she was going to stay in that barn.

We tried again. The same thing happened. Once she was through the barn doors she went berserk. My bucket of water went flying and I got the feeling we'd be there forever trying to calve her like this.

'I don't understand this at all,' said Terry. 'I've been here nearly six months now and I've never seen any of Mr Norman's cows behave like this.'

'In the daytime, yes.'

Terry and I jumped. Peter Norman had got out of bed disturbed by all the rumpus. We'd not heard him crossing the farmyard in the dark and he took us by surprise. 'At night you'll never get a cow in there. They're all the same. Have been for years.'

Together we calved Molly in the yard. It wasn't the best place for a calving. The wind and the rain off the moor was freezing and I was worried the calf would die from exposure if we weren't careful. Come to think of it, I wasn't too warm either.

'We'll put them in the shippon with the other cattle. They'll be fine in there till morning,' Peter said as we helped the tiny heifer calf to her legs. There are shippons on nearly all the Dartmoor barns. Years ago the farmers and their families lived in them with their cattle. I suppose it cut down on the central heating bills. These days the cows and the sheep have them to themselves. They're usually warm and cosy places. Just the thing when you're caught in the middle of a Dartmoor storm.

'My grandfather told me the barn was haunted, you see, Mr Taylor. Some old-time farmworker who got killed when a piece of farm equipment he was mending fell on him. My grandfather remembered the accident happening. Anyway from that day to this the cows won't go near the place at night.'

'Go away,' I said incredulously.

'No, it's true. We've even tried putting sheep in there and bolting the door at night. In the morning you'd think the poor things had been chased all over the moor by a pack of dogs. You just can't leave an animal in there. I should have told Terry but I didn't like to worry the lad.'

I wish he'd told me too. I'd always felt a bit strange when I arrived at Trowlesworthy on a call. Nothing you could put your finger on, but there was something. A sort of chill about the place that made you come out in goose pimples. I'd never said anything but I'd obviously been right. The animals felt that way too.

'He won't go anywhere near that utility room. We put his bed out there near the washing machine and tumble dryer, but he won't go near the place. He'll walk right round the house to avoid that room.'

I knew how Rebel the Alsatian felt. The Pearsons' house was on the edge of Watership Down. I was doing a locum for a vet nearby and I'd come to see Rebel who wasn't very well. The house had a long drive with lovely grounds. There was a couple of tennis courts and a swimming pool. Lovely, I thought as I made my way to the front door. But then suddenly I wasn't so sure.

Mr Pearson showed me through the house. Rebel was in the kitchen. Something in the utility room was preoccupying him. He stood in the kitchen doorway, hackles raised, growling at something. Something none of us could see. But I could feel it all right. A chill, just like that chill at Trowlesworthy farm. If you stood in the middle of the utility room it seemed freezing. No wonder Rebel was upset. He could see a ghost.

Veterinary students sometimes see ghosts too. Just outside Horrabridge on the edge of Dartmoor, not far from Tavistock, is a beautiful old Jacobean manor house. I have no idea who lives there now but when I was seeing practice with Cameron Scott, Kathy Smart and her family lived there.

Kathy was in her third year at Cambridge Veterinary School and one night after surgery I went back with her to the manor house to have a few drinks with her and her parents.

'It's haunted,' I said as soon as we walked through the main door. 'There's a real chill in the air.'

Kathy smiled comfortingly. 'Don't worry. There's nothing here that can hurt you. Most weekends we hear a ball or a banquet in full swing – you know, people dancing, singing and generally enjoying themselves.'

'Oh really,' I said anxiously. 'You're having me on, aren't you?'

'No way,' Kathy said affirmatively. 'They're real enough. So's the black dog that I've been seeing for years, ever since I was a child.'

Every night a black dog used to appear and run into her bedroom. It would sit for a while and then jump up on her bed. Some ghosts are no fools. Kathy was very pretty.

*

One night years later I was staying at a vet's house in a village near Bath. He was away for a couple of weeks and I was looking after his practice. His housekeeper and her husband, Fred, were looking after me. It was a great locum. The practice was easy to run and every night after work Fred and I would spend hours putting the world to rights at the Coach and Horses. In fact we were there so often I began to wonder if his wife thought I was a drunk.

One night we got back to the house at about eleven-thirty and I went straight to my room and bed.

I couldn't sleep. For about two hours Fred and his wife were up and down the stairs, laughing and shouting. Doors slammed. Music played and I was getting really cheesed off.

Next morning, Fred and his wife weren't very happy. 'What on earth were you doing last night, Nigel?' she demanded as I bumped into her on the upstairs landing. 'Did you bring some friends back or something? What a row. Me and Fred couldn't sleep for ages. Some people have no consideration.'

With that she turned and stormed off to the kitchen to prepare breakfast. I suddenly realised that we'd both heard the same thing. Perhaps the party had moved on from Kathy Smart's. I was just about to explain to Fred's wife about our phantom guests when there was a loud scream from the kitchen below.

'*Aargh*! It's Amber. She's dead.'

There in her basket lay Amber, the vet's old Labrador. She had been fine the day before. But there she was as dead as could be. Perhaps she'd had a heart attack. The truth was I didn't have a clue, but I couldn't help having the uneasy feeling that Amber might have been just as aware of our ghostly visitors as Fred, his wife and me. Had they scared her, or had they come for her? I'll never know. I was leaving that night, thank goodness.

Mrs Sutton was pressing me for an answer.

'Do you believe in ghosts, Mr Taylor? People think I'm barmy but I was sure you'd understand me.'

'Let's just put it this way, Mrs Sutton,' I replied. 'I don't pretend to have any of the answers. But I'll tell you this: animals know a lot more about these things than you and I ever will. Oh, and another thing. I hope you and Tuppence never need me round at your house late at night.'

'Why's that?' she asked concernedly.

'Well,' I said, 'I'll let you into a little secret. I'm afraid of the dark.'

18

If this was horse practice, great. Dick Thompson and I wanted more. Like most veterinary students we'd spent a lot of time learning about dogs and cats and the mysterious goings-on inside cows' bellies. But now the time had come to try our hand at being real horse doctors. And on this fine midsummer morning it seemed like one of the best ideas we'd ever had. Our patient was an elderly chestnut mare. She was lame but our attempts at a precise diagnosis were coming a poor second to our clinical appraisal of her owner.

Molly Wright, I suppose, you could describe as stunning. In her twenties she'd been one of the most sought-after models in the business and now, retired from the world of high fashion, she was as attractive as ever. It certainly made a change from the usual, less than aesthetic, agricultural client we were accustomed to seeing. There was no doubt about it: we were concentrating more on her bikini-clad shape than on any diagnosis.

'Right lads,' Ron Hainesworth, the equine vet we were seeing practice with, enquired with a smile, 'which one is it, right or left?'

'I wouldn't like to make a choice,' Dick replied

without hesitation as Molly trotted her horse to and fro. 'They both look good to me.'

Ron Hainesworth was a bit of an equine specialist and I think Dick and I must have impressed him with our selfless devotion to the veterinary art because the next few weeks were some of the best Dick and I had as students. He couldn't keep me and the equally eager Liverpool student away from all his horsey patients and their invariably pretty owners.

To tell you the truth, I've always found working with horses a bit dodgy. They're lovely animals but you've got to treat them with respect.

One summer early in my veterinary course I spent time on a large country estate not far from Modbury. I'd only been there for a day or two when one of the girl grooms came running into the tack room where I was busy polishing some harness.

'Nigel, come quick. Do you know anything about people bleeding from the mouth? It's Mrs Ferguson. She's been hit by a horse.'

Chloe Ferguson and her husband were top horse breeders. Their lovely animals had won every award going for years at the Devon County Show and Chloe had made a big name for herself as a very successful judge. She'd been in a stable grooming a skittish young three-year-old when for no apparent reason he reared up and knocked her flying. As he came down he'd hit her very badly around the head and she was seriously hurt.

For a moment I thought she was going to die as she lay on the stable floor. She was babbling blood from her mouth and it was pretty obvious from the dark blue blood collecting under her skin around her eyes that she'd probably fractured her skull.

'If the blacksmith had shod this horse on Monday, she'd be dead now,' her husband exclaimed. 'Thank God he couldn't get near him. The metal shoes would have killed her.'

I rolled Chloe over into the coma position so she wouldn't choke on her own blood and sent Karen, the groom, to phone the nearest doctor. He was there within minutes and realising the seriousness of Chloe's injuries he performed an emergency tracheotomy there and then. He probably saved her life.

Soon an ambulance arrived in the yard. It was full of outpatients going to one of the local hospitals. They were bundled off unceremoniously and moments later Chloe, her husband and the doctor were hurrying away to Plymouth. I was pretty shaken by all this. I'd only been working with horses for two days. That afternoon I picked the biggest horses I could and groomed them all over. I thought if I don't go near a horse today I never will.

Next day my father gave me a lift to the stables. As we drove down the narrow lane to the yard we were stopped by two men. They each had a hand-held radio and there, under their jackets, you could easily see the distinctive outline of a weapon. It was the SAS.

Chloe's son-in-law had arrived. He'd flown in by helicopter. Everywhere he goes he's protected by the SAS as once he served as a high ranking officer in

Northern Ireland and is still a target. For the next few weeks Karen and I went about our work at the stables with an armed guard. Most afternoons Chloe's son-in-law brought us tea on a silver salver. This was the life. We had a great time talking horses but all too soon he was gone, the SAS guarding his helicopter as it lifted off. Years later I saw him on a BBC documentary about army life. As he came into the room every officer in the place stood up to salute him. I hadn't realised how big a man he was. If only all those officers could have seen him down in the stable bringing us our afternoon tea.

It took Chloe nearly two years to get better. For a while she was paralysed down one side of her body, just as though she'd had a stroke. She fought her way back, though, and now you'll often see her driving her big horse box around all the West Country shows. But there was one thing I learnt. When it comes to horses you can't be too careful.

Ron Hainesworth fancied himself as a bit of an inventor. One of his pet projects was an electronic stethoscope. You see, it's pretty easy to listen to a horse's chest when it's standing still in a stable but sometimes it's only when they're exercised that breathing problems show up. If you can find a way of listening in on the move, then it's got to be a big advance.

'I'm doing some trials, lads. I need a volunteer,' he'd said to us one day as we drove back from the Devon and Exeter races. 'Nothing too complex. If you can stay upright in the saddle for more than five minutes at the trot that's fine.'

Dick volunteered at once. 'Anything to push the frontiers of veterinary medicine forward, Mr Hainesworth. I'd consider it an honour.' And I thought people only talked like that on *Startrek*.

The next day as I watched him sitting uncomfortably astride an ominously quiet, enormous bay gelding, anything less like a veterinary pioneer would have been hard to imagine. 'Wired for sound' would have been an understatement. He was festooned with electronics. From every pocket, wires and multicoloured gadgetry dangled precariously over Dick's body. He was trying hard to remain scientifically detached but, to me, he looked less like *Tomorrow's World*'s RoboVet, more like Worzel Gummidge.

The electronic stethoscope was strapped to the gelding's throat and wires connected it to all the circuitry Dick was carrying. The final adjustments were made and we were ready for the off. I stood in the middle of the field with a hand-held dish receiver, and as Dick started to gently trot around the edges of the lush Devon pasture I began to track him as if he were some orbiting alien planet.

It certainly looked impressive, though I'm not altogether sure if the three-foot aerial which reached up to the heavens from the top of his hard hat added to his stature or made him look even more like a Christmas tree on horseback. Ron was delighted. The electronic stethoscope was transmitting perfectly. Every breath the gelding took you could hear perfectly. A bit like those funny phone calls you sometimes get.

'Splendid, splendid,' shouted Ron jubilantly. 'I knew it would work.'

Suddenly we lost radio contact with Dick. The gelding had been startled by an extraordinarily exuberant flash of feedback from the stethoscope's microphone and just decided to hop it, quick. Dick couldn't do a thing. His electronic overcoat weighed him down and he just sat there majestically swaying from side to side. Another pioneer suffering in silence for his scientific breakthrough.

An hour or so later Tom Bailey, a neighbouring farmer, led Dick back, like some new age silicon chip Sir Lancelot, into Ron's yard. We explained what we'd been up to and he listened patiently as Ron explained the electronic stethoscope to him.

'Works like a radio, you say? My mate in Newton Abbot's got just the horse for one of they.'

'You see,' exclaimed Dick, ' a customer already. Brilliant.'

'Oh yeah,' said the farmer. 'Last time out he was so far behind the rest of the field that if he'd had a ruddy radio at least he could have kept in touch with 'em.'

19

'She's never going to walk again, Mr Taylor, is she?'

Sid Swift was close to tears as he gently cradled his tiny paralysed dachshund in his massive arms. It seemed hardly five minutes ago that Sid had brought her to me as a puppy for her first injections against distemper and parvovirus.

'Not my sort of dog at all, you understand,' he'd said at the time, 'but now that I'm retired from the railway my wife says I need an interest. We've only got a small home, so here she is, Izzy.'

I liked Sid. He'd been a fireman on the old Great Western Railway and so we had a lot in common. My dad had worked on the railway too as a guard, and just before I went off to study at university I'd worked at Plymouth North Road Station as a porter.

You'd be amazed how many diagnostic skills you can learn on the railway. Mind you, I had a good teacher. Arthur Flack. To Arthur working with parcels was a bit like clinical medicine is to me today, one big guessing game.

'What's this, then? Go on, go on, guess,' he'd say as he'd pick up a parcel from the great pile we were unloading from a heavily laden parcels van. 'It's easy. Go on. Go on, guess.'

Then there'd be a little ritual as I scratched my head and ran through a list of all the possible treasures the parcel might contain. 'Hair dryer, pullover, spark plugs, cuddly toy?' I'd say like a happy winner on *The Generation Game*.

'No, never,' he'd say with glee, flourising the triangular package. 'Black and Decker power drill. Gets you every time.'

Years later I was in my final examinations when one of the surgeons pushed an anatomical specimen my way. I must have looked blank as he waited for my answer.

'Go on, go on, guess,' he said impatiently.

I'm still not convinced 'Black and Decker power drill' was the reply he expected.

Whenever Sid came to see me he'd bring along a few old photos of the trains he used to work on and we'd talk railways while outside in the consulting room the rest of the clients waited. But not today. Izzy was in too much pain.

'I think she's slipped a disc, Sid,' I said as I carefully examined the little dog. 'It's quite common in the breed but there's no real reason why she shouldn't be better again soon. I'll have to take some X-rays to be sure.'

I don't know who designed dachshunds, but whoever it was didn't get it quite right. They've got very long backs with a pair of legs stuck almost as an afterthought on each end. A bit like a walking suspension bridge. In fact if you've ever seen that film of a Californian suspension bridge tearing itself apart in a storm way back in the 1930s then you've got a pretty good idea of what a dachshund's back is doing as it walks along. It's bobbing about all over the place. No wonder they slip discs from time to time.

'She's a so-and-so for jumping into the back of my car. I bet she did it then,' Sid said as he comforted the little dog with a pat on the head.

The X-rays showed that one of Izzy's lumbar discs was causing the trouble. Its sudden displacement was leading to inflammation and swelling which was pressing on her spinal cord. This meant the nerves to her hind legs were being pinched and so Izzy couldn't walk.

'Are you going to operate on her?' Sid asked me when I gave him the news.

'No, Sid. I don't think we'll have to. Some pain killing injections and some anti-inflammatory steroids will help. Then it's just time. You'll have to nurse her of course, but I'm sure that's no problem.'

'Oh no Mr Taylor, no problem at all. Nothing but the best for her.'

I knew Sid would do what he could and, sure enough, over the next few weeks he nursed Izzy splendidly. I'm always impressed by the care and devotion shown by owners of sick and injured animals, but it takes a special effort to look after a paralysed dog. It took about two weeks before we saw much of an improvement with Izzy. When I pinched her toes she could obviously feel it and she was starting to make weak, fumbling attempts to use her disabled hind legs. Sid was pleased, but watching Izzy dragging herself around his home was clearly upsetting him.

'I know, Sid,' I told him the next time I saw Izzy, 'why don't we give Izzy her own set of wheels. We'll build her a little cart to support her hind legs and then she'll be able to get about much better.'

I'd seen quite a few of these carts when I was in Canada, working as a surgeon at the Ontario Veterinary College. We'd often have three or four paraplegic dachshunds to care for. Some had surgery, some didn't. It just depended on their problems. One thing they all had was wheels. On quiet Wednesday afternoons the interns would sneak off and find the longest corridors in the vet school and we'd have chariot races as the little dogs sprinted furiously around the place. Ben Hur, eat your heart out. They loved it, and I'm sure their mobility gave them a bit of hope and helped them on their way back to full recovery. A cart could be just what Izzy needed.

'A friend of mine who used to work with the engines at Laira depot has knocked this up. What do you think, Mr Taylor?' Sid asked me as he proudly showed me the little cart made from some bent metal bars and some old skateboard wheels. 'Her legs slip into these holes either side at the back and she's got all the support she needs. She's off like a rocket given half the chance.'

Izzy seemed delighted with her new mobility as

she tore around the surgery scrabbling like a demon with her front legs to build up speed. I hadn't seen her so happy for weeks. It took about six weeks before she was fully recovered. Sid brought her back for a couple of check-ups and every time I could feel the strength returning to her legs as the inflammation in her spine subsided and her nervous system started to work properly again. Soon she was almost as good as new and could walk happily again with no discomfort.

She didn't want to give up her skateboard, though.

A few months later I was at Staverton Station on the line from Buckfastleigh to Totnes. I love it there. It's an old Great Western line that's been preserved and operates with steam just like it used to when Sid and my dad first started working on the trains.

I was waiting for the mid-afternoon train, probably a pannier tank with a few old coaches, when across the platform came the sound of barking. It was Sid and Izzy.

'We often come up here,' the old railwayman said. 'I love the trains and Izzy gets a great run on this platform with her skateboard. She still loves riding around on it even though she doesn't really need it any more.'

'There you are Sid, I told you Isabel would be all right.'

'Isabel?' he replied with more than a hint of surprise in his voice. 'I thought you would have guessed. After all I'm an old Great Western man. She's called Izzy after Brunel. Isambard Kingdom Brunel.'

I smiled as Sid continued his explanation.

'Bit like you, Brunel. He knew a thing or two about suspension bridges!'

20

It's not easy being one of the last romantics.

Justin Palethorpe was having a pretty good try, though. After all, ever since he moved to Cornwall in the mid-sixties he'd done little else but write poetry – and keep goats. Mind you, as far as Ernie and I were concerned, Justin wasn't so much romantic as aromatic.

'He stinks,' Ernie whispered slyly to me as we crossed the farmyard. 'Goats and garlic, what a combination. No wonder being a poet is such a lonely business.'

I've known Ernie for years. We met at a friend's wedding and found we both shared a love of animals and the country. Ernie's a kidney patient and spends a lot of his time on dialysis machines. Getting out and about in the splendid Cornish countryside with me meant a lot to him. Most weekends he'd ride shotgun in my car as we'd travel round the Cornish farms. He'd spend the long days helping me with my veterinary work which he loved.

But judging by the look of discomfort on his face, this was one weekend trip he could have done without. If only I'd remembered how much Justin like garlic.

'Back to nature, Mr Taylor. We'd all be much healthier if our lives were a little more herbal. Too many chemicals about these days. I mean take a look at the ozone layer and what's happened to that. Don't you agree?' he'd said when we first met.

He had asked me for advice on how to worm his goats but he'd been most put out when I suggested one of the splendid new wormers that I knew worked so well.

'No way am I using anything that's got a single chlorinated hydrocarbon in it,' he said when I showed him the bottle. 'If that's the best you can do I'll stick to crushed garlic. It's natural you know, so it's got to be best.'

Just my luck that he'd been an industrial chemist before he'd turned to flower power. I couldn't argue with his science and the strange thing was that he was right. His goats never got worms.

'I'm not surprised,' Ernie said when I told him. 'If I was a worm you wouldn't catch me within a mile of any goat eating garlic. *Ugh*! Talk about bad breath. If one of them opened its mouth it could kill a dentist at ten yards.'

But today Ernie and I had a stroke of luck. Justin's goats were fine, we wouldn't have to go too close to them. We could breathe again. One of Justin's geese had a broken wing and he thought I'd be just the man to splint it.

'Car accident, you say? You're dead right. It's busted.' I turned to Ernie who was holding the goose as tight as he could and trying to stop it from attacking me. 'Good job you're here, mate. You're always saying you're a bit of an expert with birds. Here's your chance.'

I hurried to the car to fetch all the sticking plaster, bandage and cotton wool we might need. When I returned, Ernie and Justin were trying to recapture the goose who, noticing a sudden lapse of concentration when Ernie had caught a whiff of natural goodness from the poet's direction, had made a break for freedom. Luckily its injured wing trailing on the ground stopped it from getting too far and they soon caught up with it. Interestingly enough Justin came out with a few pretty unromantic expletives at this point. But then the artistic temperament can often be a bit strained, especially if a goose has just bitten you on the bum.

'Right Ernie,' I said as we finally got it back under control. 'If Justin holds it still, you and I will splint its wing.'

I always knew I should have been in the St John Ambulance. Ernie and I did a great job. It took about twenty minutes. The goose wasn't pleased and remained aggressively uncooperative thoughout, but when we had finished, the right wing was enclosed in a bulging cocoon of cotton wool and sticking plaster. Justin released the goose and Ernie and I stood back in silent admiration of our efforts. Justin wasn't impressed for long.

'Why does he keep walking around like that? And another thing, can't you see he can only walk around in circles? A tipsy goose isn't much good to me,' Justin exclaimed.

Justin was right. The splint was a marvel of Ernie's ingenuity but it was just too heavy for the startled bird. As it continued to circle the farm yard in an ever decreasing clockwork orbit, we held a conference.

'Take it off and start again,' Ernie finally decided. 'You can't win them all. Good bit of first aid though, wasn't it?'

'Certainly was,' I agreed, 'but this time we'll cut out the heroics and just try a couple of pieces of tape around the goose's body. That should splint the injured wing and if we're lucky the goose won't be falling about all over the place.'

'I hope it works,' said Justin. 'A poet can only be pecked so often.'

This time we were luckier. We unravelled Ernie's marvellous contraption and the goose stayed relatively peaceful as I wrapped some tape around its middle to trap the injured wing.

'Put him down, Ernie. We'll see if he can waddle straight now.'

Justin was happier this time. The goose trundled off into the distance without a wobble.

'It'll take a few weeks but the wing should heal. You can take the tape off then. Good luck,' I told the bemused poet as I gathered up my bits and pieces and got ready to leave.

'We could have saved ourselves a lot of bother if we'd borrowed some of his garlic,' Ernie announced as we drove away back towards Liskeard. 'I hear garlic makes good stuffing.'

'I don't think Justin or his goose would have appreciated that,' I said. 'Mind you, it would have taught that ruddy bird a lesson.'

Ernie turned to me and with an evil grin, declared enthusiastically, 'Poetic justice'.

21

I was beginning to think Charlie Bishop would never hear me. I'd been knocking on his door for about five minutes, but there still wasn't a sign of life.

I knew Charlie was in. For one thing his radio was going full blast and every now and then I'd catch the sound of a rich Devonian voice stretched to its musical limit.

'Don't be cruel to a heart,' then a quivering pause, building up to a final burst, 'To a heart that's true.' Dartmoor is an awful long way from Memphis, Tennessee but it was pretty obvious from the shepherd's unrestrained vocal enthusiasm that I had stumbled across one of Elvis Presley's biggest fans.

I should have guessed, really. The battered sign on the farm gate was a big give-away. 'Welcome to Graceland', it screamed in vivid blue-green letters.

Charlie was still humming when he finally realised I was outside waiting. He was right in the middle of lambing and two ewes were in trouble. Charlie was convinced the only way we'd save the lambs and deliver them was by Caesarean.

'Never thought of you as a Golden Oldie, Charlie,' I said as we walked across the farmyard to the waiting sheep. 'I didn't think you had that much time for pop music.'

'You can keep the rest,' he replied with a self-conscious smile. 'As far as I'm concerned there's only one real pop star. The King. Miss him a lot, I do. Still, we've got his music. I know all the words, every one.'

Charlie also knew a lot about sheep. Sure enough we had to deliver their lambs by Caesarean and it wasn't too long before three more joined the bleating chorus which seemed to fill Charlie's barn from floor to roof. There were sheep everywhere, Cheviot crosses and whiteface Dartmoors. One great big, woolly maternity ward, a sure sign spring was on its way. Just as I was about to leave for home, Charlie called me over to one corner of the farmyard and opened the door to a small stable and proudly showed me one of his favourite dogs, Bracken and her new litter of puppies.

One of the tiny black and white bundles was so full of life that he was obviously going to be the pick of the bunch. Charlie had already decided to keep him and train him as a working dog.

'A real champion. I can tell he's going to do well,' he murmured excitedly. And then he added with sudden delight. 'I think he deserves a winning name. I'll call him Elvis.'

I'm a big fan of border collies too. In fact I became a vet because of one. Her name was Rusty. She was a red and white collie and she was gorgeous. My mum and dad found her in Victoria Park just after the war.

There were lots of abandoned dogs around in Plymouth just then. I suppose with all the upheavals of the war the last thing people could care for sometimes were their pets. Rusty was in a bad way. She was very thin and could hardly walk.

'She won't last more than a day or so,' the policeman said when my mum took her along to the nearest police station. 'If I was you I'd have her put to sleep. It would be the kindest thing.'

Before the war my mum had spent some time helping out with the PDSA clinics. If anyone could help, the PDSA would.

Norman King, the vet there, wasn't very optimistic. 'It'll be touch and go for a long while. But if you're prepared to help her, so will I.'

It took them eighteen months. At first she was too weak to walk anywhere so my mum and dad borrowed an old pram and wheeled her to the PDSA for her regular visits. Soon she started to improve and one of the best photos I've got is of Rusty winning a PDSA dog show a year or two after she got well.

When I was young my parents would walk the five miles or so out of Plymouth and up onto Roborough Down. Rusty would trot alongside my pram, and as I grew up we were inseparable. I'm told I learnt to walk as patiently, time and time again, she'd support me as my balance got better.

One day we all took the Torpoint ferry and went across to Whitsands beach in Cornwall. There was panic for a while. Rusty had disappeared. A busy bank holiday beach and she was nowhere to be seen.

Suddenly my mother heard a man calling her name. He was waving frantically. Beside him sat a red and white Border collie, pleased as punch with herself. There amongst all those hundreds of people she'd found the one person who'd helped her when she was ill. Norman King.

I can't remember how old I was when Rusty became ill again. She was in a bad way. Vomiting all the time and making a terrible mess. I had an old *Rupert* annual that meant a lot to me. I couldn't help her any other way, so I tore it up and cleaned her with its pages. Not long after that she died. I still miss her. That's why I became a vet.

Elvis was a real natural. At first he'd watch all the other collies at work and then, in his puppy way, he'd round up everything that moved on the farm. Visiting vets were good for practice too. He did meet his match once, though, when he tried to persuade Charlie's geese they'd be better off in the barn than in the duckpond. The geese moved all right but it wasn't long before they gained the upper hand and Elvis found himself jumping into the pond to get away from them.

Charlie was delighted with his progress and spent hours with him, patiently training and preparing him for the sheepdog trials all the moorland farmers enjoy. But, just as Elvis seemed to be reaching the peak of his young life, an accident happened which nearly broke Charlie's heart.

'One minute he was running across the moor, full of beans. Then suddenly he turned awkward like and fell screaming to the floor. Screaming like a stuck pig he was, Mr Taylor,' Charlie told me anxiously. 'I thought he'd been shot. It's his right back leg. He can't walk. I just don't understand it.' Charlie was dejected as I examined the injured sheepdog.

Luckily Elvis's leg wasn't broken. He'd torn the ligaments in his knee, or stifle. I took some X-rays to be sure but it was soon pretty obvious from the way I could manipulate the leg under anaesthetic that he had a ruptured cruciate ligament. It's a common injury but pretty painful. Sometimes dogs get better with rest alone but Elvis was far too lively for that. Surgery could be the answer.

Charlie wasn't very enthusiastic. 'I don't want Elvis operated on.'

But when I explained that if Elvis was ever going to work again we had to repair the damaged ligament he understood.

'Just get on with it.'

At the time vets used a piece of nylon thread to repair the damaged ligament. Today we use a different technique which lets us use a part of the undamaged patellar ligament to form a natural graft. But my nylon thread worked just as well and it wasn't long before Elvis was on the mend. Mind you, it wasn't easy to persuade him to take it easy for the month or so his leg was healing.

Charlie was delighted with his bionic dog. Soon Elvis seemed to be able to use his leg normally and it wasn't long before the two of them were back out on the moor practising for the sheepdog trials.

The following summer I was at the trials congratulating Charlie on owning the champion dog when a pretty young girl came up to us and started to ask Charlie all about Elvis and how he'd been trained.

'I suppose it's easy training a special animal like this,' she said enthusiastically.

'Oh, he ain't nothing special miss,' Charlie replied modestly. He paused and then giving me a knowing smile, he continued. 'In fact, he ain't nothing but a hound dog!'

22

'Can you come and give us a talk?'

I've always had a great deal of respect for experts. Gifted teachers and exponents of the perennial mysteries of science and philosophy who, with casual asides and restrained understatement, allow us ordinary mortals a tantalising glimpse of the cosmic forces that guide us all, from mitochondria to marathon men.

So, when my chance came to add an inch or two to the Ascent of Man, or as it turned out the Ascent of the local Working Dogs Society, I could not refuse.

Luckily for me and most vets, the Renaissance scholars largely left the care and welfare of the whelping bitch alone as a subject of intense study. I'm told Leonardo da Vinci might have had a stab at it but I suppose, compared to designing helicopters and capturing a virgin's smile on canvas, it comes a pretty poor third. This probably explains why, even today, the most experienced dog breeder seems to find the whole thing a complete mystery and so keeps the veterinary profession in business as the masters of midwifery.

'You've not filled that in properly. I can just about read your name but there's no mention of your breed,' said the society's secretary. She had asked me to sign the register of attendance and then hovered accusingly behind me as my signature filled the empty page. 'I've had my eye on you. First you arrive late. I've never seen you before and you won't even tell me what breed you're involved with. This isn't the Kennel Club. You're not from the council, are you? A lot of them are anti-dog you know.'

'I'm your guest speaker,' I mumbled feebly. 'I don't breed dogs, working or unemployed. I'm on next, when you've finished your AGM. Business before pleasure, you might say.'

Then again you might not. I'm still not sure she really heard me anyway, because just then the chairman announced the end of the afternoon's painfully protracted proceedings. This is it, I thought. The Big Announcement.

'Now that we've dispensed with all your – ' madam chairman paused resignedly, ' – points of order, we can move onto the main highlight of the afternoon. What you've all been waiting for . . .'

An excited air of anticipation filled the hall at this news. Great, I couldn't have expected a better introduction. I sat back and waited for the applause to break out like thunder from my eagerly expectant audience.

'. . . Mrs Treadwell's cherry tarts and tea!'

There was a sudden rush for the beckoning Bakewells and as I've never been one to miss out on a free feed I joined the jostling queue. After all, if top breeders recommended them, they had to be good.

The buffet wasn't at all bad and I introduced myself to the charming chairman who graciously explained she'd been expecting an older man, and where was my tweed jacket? But now she'd realised I was their speaker, we could begin. A short introduction was all I really needed.

'Ladies and gentlemen. This is Mr, um, er, TURNER! He's very kindly going to tell us what to do with our whelping bitches.'

There was a polite ripple of applause as I rose to speak. Then, nothing, not a murmur as I deftly explained the unknown intricacies of uterine inertia and the subtle diversions of labour. I felt sure they were enjoying my talk but it was hard to tell. Marcel Marceau would have been a noisier audience.

'Are there any questions? I'll do my best to answer any you might have,' I assured them.

'What are your current thoughts on early embryonic death in smooth coated retrievers? Does parvovirus have any effect on premature mortality?'

It was Mrs Treadwell. Just my luck to meet a closet embryologist.

'Not a lot of research has been done into this worrying problem.' She seemed satisfied with some further tremulous explanations on the vagaries of canine implantation. In fact my increasingly appreciative audience visibly perked up when I mentioned implantation.

After that, there was no stopping them. Questions flew my way. I think we covered every aspect from premature expectation to overdue lactation. All features, great and small. There were a couple of sticky moments when veterinary fees were mentioned. Why was there such a variation in how much Caesareans cost from area to area?

'Geographical overheads,' I mumbled. 'Talk it over with your own vets. They'll explain.'

'Thank you, Mr TANNER. I'm sure that answers all our questions. I'm so looking forward to my next labour,' said the chairman as the questions came to a close.

I couldn't be absolutely sure but I didn't think congratulations were needed. It was time to leave. Someone mentioned more points of order and the Working Dogs settled down for another session of heated debate.

'Not bad for a beginner.' I'd almost made it to the car when Mrs Treadwell collared me. 'I think we'll have you back. We normally have that awfully nice Mr Welcome from down the road but he's on a sponsored walk this weekend. Pity really. He always entertains us.'

I smiled politely and wondered why I hadn't disappeared jogging with Jimmy Herbert. This learned expert trip was fraught with failure. No wonder the other vet had headed for the hills.

'Mind you,' she said reflectively, 'sometimes entertainment isn't everything. Education, that's what breeders need. And you've certainly educated us all this afternoon. I think you deserve a special reward for all your efforts.'

Mrs Treadwell beamed enthusiastically and handed me a small package. 'Have a cherry Bakewell.'

23

It was probably easier getting blood out of a stone than out of Hugh Meavy's Galloways.

I liked Hugh. He'd been in the Navy for years. Mind you, I hoped he'd managed better with mine-sweepers than he did with Dartmoor cattle. When it came to cows, Hugh Meavy was all at sea.

It was easy liking Hugh. For one thing he looked upon all his cattle as 'jolly fine chaps'. It could be a little strange arriving on his farm not far from Clear-brook and being told, 'That chap over there isn't giving as much milk as he should.'

And then there were Hugh's little emergencies.

'One of my chaps is in labour,' he told me on the telephone late one night. 'You'd better come soon. When a chap's in trouble he needs a vet.'

The chap was a delicate Jersey cow which with a bit of help from Hugh and me gave birth to a fine pair of twins. Two lovely chaps! I was beginning to wonder if Hugh was cut out to be a farmer.

He soon found dairy farming a little more than he bargained for and proudly announced to me one misty September morning that he was going to do his bit for Queen and Country. 'What this nation needs is protein. And I'm the man to provide it. From now on it's beef. Great chaps, beef cattle. Salt of the earth.'

I told him I thought it was a good idea. After all, beef cattle don't need as much looking after as dairy cows with their endless daily routine of milking. But I was a little concerned when he told me he was buying some Galloways from Archie Flood. Galloways aren't my favourite patient. They may be hardy little characters, ideal for Dartmoor and its bleak wilderness, but when it comes to being handled they've got about as much charm as a Glasgow street fighter. Real toughs. They move like greased lightning and can give you more bruises per minute than any breed of cow I've ever met. All Galloways are pretty wild but Archie Flood's would have won a prize for solid aggression and meanness, any day.

Archie himself couldn't have been more gentle and easy going. The sort of helpful farmer who was always at hand when his neighbours needed help. So I wasn't surprised to see Archie and his two sons waiting with Hugh at the Clearbrook farm when I arrived for Hugh's brucellosis blood test.

Brucellosis is an unpleasant disease which causes abortion in cattle. It's no joke for vets and farmers either. Lots of us have caught it over the years. It causes a fever which keeps coming back, month after month. Cameron Scott used to have it badly. Once every three or four weeks he'd take to his bed, shivering even on the hottest day. Whisky and the *Financial Times* helped him a bit but he was ill for years. Most treatment for brucellosis with antibiotics is pretty ineffective. The plan was to eradicate it from the national herd so that nobody could catch it and the cows themselves would remain healthy. Most of the country was already clear, but the far Southwest hung out for a long time. Any cows that came positive on the blood test were slaughtered. In some Cornish farms I'd seen whole herds of pedigree animals disappear overnight. Today we'd see how Hugh's Galloways got on. But first I had to get some blood. All Hugh's 'chaps' had to be tested. The thought of wrestling with a hundred hairy hardnuts filled me with despair. I should have stayed in bed.

For one thing it was raining. It always rains when I blood test cattle. For years now I've been convinced that Craig Rich, the West Country television weatherman, has got my every move pinpointed on his meteorological maps. If there's a chance of a deep depression anywhere this side of the Bay of Biscay it always seems to head my way.

It used to rain when I went blood testing in the Highlands too. But there were compensations. 'You'll need a guide to find all these crofts,' Anthony Hadrian had told me one morning. 'I've arranged for Hamish McLeod to meet you at the Snoddys'. He'll go round with you the rest of the day.'

Hamish McLeod could turn his hand to most things. When I first arrived in the Highlands I thought he ran the local post office. He did. Then I was out on a call one day when I saw him painting and decorating. In his spare time he was the local undertaker and wedding photographer but today he was Sherpa Tenzing to my Edmund Hillary. He would guide me around the crofts.

'You'll be having a small one, then,' old Mrs Snoddy said when I'd finished testing her two cows. 'Hamish and the vets always have a wee dram to keep their spirits up when they're out testing.'

Hamish smiled and gave me a knowing wink. 'It's a great life, the veterinary one,' he said enthusiastically, 'especially if you like the malt.' He drained his glass of whisky with a single swallow.

'You'll have another, Mr McLeod. Afore ye go.'

It was an awful long time afore we went. Hamish settled back in the armchair and caught up on all the gossip he'd missed since the last blood test a year before. I was amazed that there was so much for him and Mrs Snoddy to gossip about. As far as I could see there were more sheep and cattle than people in the Highlands, but what few people there were must have been very active if Hamish's tales of lurid goings on were anything to go by.

'It's the long dark winter nights,' he told me as we drove to Altnaharra. 'Folk have got to keep themselves occupied somehow.'

As we drove up to Donald Hamilton's croft Hamish leant across me in the car and whispered, 'Donald's famous for his women. He advertises for them in the *Sunday Express*. Come up here by the bus load they do. Have done for years.'

Donald Hamilton emerged from his tiny cottage. He was an elderly man, mid-seventies I'd say. Tweed suited, to look at him you'd never think he was a womaniser.

'He put an advert in the *Sunday Express* years ago. Something like "Lonely, wealthy Highland landowner seeks wife". The editor at the time thought it would make a good story. They invited Donald down to London. Put him up in a big hotel they did. Scores of women came to meet him. Mind you, when some of 'em came up here and saw the croft they weren't that impressed. But Donald keeps advertising. And the women keep coming.'

'Get away,' I said incredulously.

'You don't have to believe me. Donald will show you his press cuttings. Always does. Every year.'

Sure enough once we'd blood tested Donald's only cow, an Ayrshire who'd seen better days, we sat in Donald's parlour and out came the cuttings book.

'There,' he said expansively, 'that's me at the Dorchester. The *Sunday Express* paid for it all. Great story they said, and I went along with it. More whisky?'

Hamish and I had fifteen more crofts to visit before our blood test was over. He was really enjoying himself. The ministry blood test was the highlight of his social calendar. I tried to refuse the crofters' hospitality.

'I'm driving,' I said half-heartedly sometime in the middle of the morning. 'There's no way I can carry on like this.'

It wasn't only my driving that was starting to suffer. Normally I can hit the tail vein of a cow first time. It's not that difficult. You just feel for the gaps between the coccygeal vertebrae and go for it. When it took me fifteen attempts to get some blood from Mary Cameron's Jersey I knew I'd had enough.

'I'll take you home on the tractor,' Hamish volunteered. 'It's about an hour's drive cross country.'

Mary Cameron wouldn't let him. 'My son Dougal will drive the tractor,' she said firmly. 'It's either that or ye'll both be heading back down the glen on foot.'

As the tractor bumped its lazy way home that evening Hamish and I rattled around on the trailer behind. We were getting soaked. Highland summers can be very damp. Funny, but that was the only time I've ever been blood testing when I haven't noticed the rain at all.

Not like today, back at the far southern tip of the country. It was already drizzling. Another soggy session. The labels would all peel off the little test tubes I collected the blood in. My pen would give up the ghost. Another bloody blood test.

Once I'd just finished testing three hundred Friesians at a farm near Truro. I'd left the blood samples in the dairy on top of the bulk tank. Suddenly there was an almighty crash and the sound of breaking glass. One of the farm cats couldn't resist the challenge and had swiped all my samples to the floor. Chaos. It's a good job I like cats.

Hugh's Galloways were on fine form. This was going to be a long test. Grouping together in little gangs, they refused to be driven into the cattle crush. Once you got one in it was a real game to read its ear tag as it tried to headbutt you. Then, when eventually I tried to suck some blood out of their raised tail veins, I was engulfed in a creeping brown tide. Galloways will use any weapon they've got.

Hugh Meavy was getting browned off too. I could see him becoming hot under the collar but, as always, he tried to remain cheerful. Although from time to time he'd murmur 'Bloody hell' belligerently as one of the little darlings aimed a playful kick at his groin.

Archie's sons were having a great time driving Hugh's Galloways around the farmyard. The trouble was they both fancied themselves as cowboys; Clearbrook's Clint Eastwoods. Bruce, the elder of the two, had a Western saddle and a large rawhide whip which every now and then he cracked over the heads of the rebellious Galloways.

To begin with the Galloways ignored the two horsemen and their ferocious cowboy howls, but soon they sensed that enough was enough and the Flood Boys had reached their last roundup. There was a frantic bellowing roar from the midst of the herd and the leaders of the revolt rushed headlong at Bruce Flood. Bruce's horse had seen too many Westerns to hang around taking any chances. As the Galloways surged forward it headed for the nearest hedge which it cleared like an old Aintree hand on Grand National day. Bruce clung onto his neck for dear life as he clattered away across the open fields trying to put as much distance as he could between himself and the bunch of berserk bovines in Hugh's yard.

I had watched this unexpected stampede with

growing unease. It was no time to be proud. Archie Flood and I could have outrun Linford Christie as we abandoned the blood test and sprinted for the safety of the nearest barn. Hugh was made of sterner stuff. The bulldog spirit. He stood there, Canute like in the middle of the yard, as the savage, stampeding hordes approached him.

'Now come on, chaps. Enough's enough. Play the game. You've made your point,' we heard him say as he was swallowed up in a sea of black.

We rushed to help him as soon as the stampede had passed. Miraculously, he wasn't hurt. He stood up, shook the mud from his clothes and staggered unsteadily towards me.

'Are you sure you're all right?' I asked anxiously. I felt certain we'd just witnessed the end of Hugh Meavy's Dartmoor farming days.

He looked me straight in the eye, grimaced a little with pain, then murmured, 'Bloody hell', and fainted clean away.

24

'I don't care what you say, Mr Taylor. You can go right the way round the world but you won't see a better sunset than you can see right here on Plymouth Hoe.'

I knew exactly what Percy Richards meant. I'm told Plymouth Sound is every bit as beautiful as San Francisco Bay or Sydney Harbour. The view from the Hoe is magnificent at any time of the day. But in the evening, as the sun drops in the west, leaving an orange glow over Drake's Island, with the mysterious coastline of Cornwall stretching to the horizon beyond, you can see why the people of Plymouth love it so much.

Perfect, I think the man said. Just perfect.

'Me and Cassie we come up here every night for a walk. She's my eyes now but I can still remember how beautiful the sunsets are. I never saw better, you know. And I was in the Royal Navy man and boy and travelled all over.'

I've known Percy for a few years now. I look after a lot of guide dogs. If you ask me they're the best patients I'll ever have. And to think some people don't like dogs at all. They've never met Cassie or her pals.

When Percy lost his sight through diabetes he was devastated. He told me when he first brought Cassie to me for a check-up, 'Until they sent me to Exeter and gave me Cassie I thought my world had come to an end. But, do you know, you can't be miserable with a lovely creature like this to keep you company and look after you. Worth her weight in gold, she is. Worth her weight in gold.'

The young golden retriever stood patiently while I listened to her heart and lungs and gave her a thorough clinical examination.

'Fine, just fine. I'll see you in six months' time as usual. That's if I don't bump into you and Cassie up on the Hoe one evening.'

'You're still jogging, then. Getting ready for the London Marathon? Rather him than us, eh Cassie?'

I'm not what you call a natural athlete. No, Roger Black or Sebastian Coe needn't worry. I won't be chasing their titles. These days I'm more a fun runner. Mind you, I've had my moments. The Royal Veterinary College cross-country team wasn't that bad. Clive Reid and I could run with the best of them. And often did. We'd be there with all the stars. Dave Bedford, Brendan Foster. Well, at least we'd line up with them at the start on Parliament Hill Fields. Then it was a six-mile dash to be back before your beans and pasty started turning cold. I shouldn't think Dave Bedford or Brendan Foster ever ate a cold pasty in their lives. They'd be finished, showered and gone long before Clive and I hit halfway. It's tough at the top. It's even tougher half way down the field.

I discovered running again when I wanted to lose a bit of weight. People were beginning to notice I was bulging out a bit. You know the sort of thing – when you start to look less like Robert Redford, more like the Incredible Hulk. I joined a fitness class. 'Bellywatchers'. If you're going to be a born-again belly there's no good playing at it, you've got to go for the burn.

'Why don't you try a bit of jogging?' Jim my diet guru suggested one evening when I was bouncing up and down with the rest of the Bellywatchers as Tina Turner belted out something about not wanting another hero. 'You haven't got the legs for it but the exercise will do you good. You never know you might enjoy it!'

Jim was right. It could have been the endorphins or it could have been the company, but after the first few weeks I found I was enjoying running again. And best of all I enjoyed the runs up around the Hoe.

'Lots of history round here,' Jimmy Herbert reminded me one night as we sped up and across the top of the Hoe. 'That's where they say Drake played bowls while he waited for the Spanish Armada.'

'Yes, and don't forget the Pilgrims. The *Mayflower* must have sailed right out across the Sound when they shot off to America,' I gasped as I tried to keep up with him. 'I get seasick on the Torpoint ferry so I wouldn't have been much good as a Pilgrim.'

Often we'd see Percy and Cassie. Taking their time, just enjoying the evening. And as they walked Percy would tell the dog all about his time in the Navy and how years ago when Plymouth was being bombed, people danced up on the Hoe in the evenings to show they would never be beaten by the Blitz.

'Great times, Cassie, great times. They used to have some lovely bands you know. Just like Glenn Miller. You'd have loved them.'

The next time Percy brought Cassie to the surgery for her routine six-monthly check, I could tell he was worried.

'She's not seeing too well, I'm sure of it. She keeps bumping into things. We're a fine pair. I'm ever so worried about her.'

'How old is she now?'

'About six. She's got years to go yet, Mr Taylor. What's wrong with her?'

I looked into Cassie's eyes with my opthalmoscope.

'I'm sorry, Percy, but Cassie's starting to lose her sight too. Her retina's damaged and from what I can see she's well on her way to developing cataracts.'

Some breeds of dog, and the golden retriever is one, seem more inclined to lose their sight as they get older. No one really knows why, but there's a progressive deterioration in vision as the retina at the back of the eye degenerates. There's not a lot anyone can do and over time the dog's vision fades and the once clear eyes become dull and cloudy with cataracts.

'She'll have to retire, I'm afraid,' I told him as I finished my examination. 'The Guide Dogs people do their best not to breed dogs that develop this problem, but I suppose every now and then you're still going to get one. What a shame it's poor old Cassie.'

'Don't worry, Mr Taylor, I won't give her up. She'll still have a good home with me, even if I have to get another dog.'

And that's exactly what happened. Cassie was retired and it wasn't long before Jimmy Herbert and I came across the three of them strolling along the Hoe early one summer's evening.

'This is Irma, Mr Taylor. Isn't she a beauty? I've only had her for a week or so. Another golden retriever, just like Cassie,' Percy continued proudly. 'They told me I could have had a Labrador or a German Shepherd, but no sir. I like golden retrievers. Always have.'

'She's lovely Percy,' I said as the young guide dog quietly sat beside her new master. 'How's Cassie taken to her?'

'Marvellous. Just marvellous. It's like they've always been pals. And do you know, I'm sure Irma knows Cassie's sight isn't too good either. They stick so close together I'm sure Irma is guiding her too.'

Jimmy and I watched as the happy trio ambled away from us. 'We'll have to tell Irma about Glenn Miller too, won't we, Cassie?' we heard the old man say as we ran past them back to the running club.

A few weekends later, I was seeing a few people at my Sunday morning surgery when Jimmy Herbert, still in his jogging gear came rushing into the consulting room.

'It's Irma. She's been attacked by a couple of lurchers up on the Hoe. She's in a bad way. I'm sure you'll have to stitch her up. Percy and Cassie are in the car with her now.'

Two dogs had appeared out of nowhere and before Percy could do a thing about it they'd gone for Irma. Cassie tried her best to fight them off but Irma, wearing her guide harness, hadn't had much of a chance to fight back.

'She's pretty torn, Percy, and she's lost a lot of blood. I'll operate straight away.' I reassured the worried old man that she'd be all right.

I was just about to pick Irma up and carry her away to the operating theatre when I suddenly realised I was being growled at.

'It's Cassie. She doesn't want to leave her,' Percy announced. 'If Irma goes to the theatre then Cassie and me come too.'

I've never been growled at so much during an operation. Once your patient's asleep there's usually hardly a sound. But not today. Every time I reached for a swab or some suture, a whine and a growl would remind me that her eyesight might be dodgy but Cassie was keeping an eye on me. Irma was going to survive, or else.

'Nearly done, girl,' I said as I finished suturing Irma's largest wound. 'It won't be long before she's up and about. Then you and me can be friends again.'

Jimmy, Percy and I waited as the anaesthetic gradually wore off and Irma groggily recovered. Cassie paced the room anxiously and threw me a warning glance every now and then.

'There, now you can make a fuss of her. She's going to be fine,' I said as I helped Irma to her feet.

Cassie rushed to her friend's side and began nuzzling her furiously. The growling stopped and her tail started wagging as if it was going to fall off any moment. I don't think I've ever felt so appreciated. Cassie was happy again.

You can still see the three of them most evenings if you take a trip to Plymouth Hoe. Cassie's a bit slower now so Irma takes her time as she guides Percy towards the sunset. I often stop and pat them both if I'm jogging by. They're always pleased to see me, especially Cassie who insists on giving me her paw before I go. It's great to be friends again.

25

If Barry Snowdon said you were good, you were good. I don't suppose it's easy being the hero of every veterinary student in the final year but Barry took it in his stride. But then again he made everything he did look easy. Especially colics.

'There's a colic coming in,' Debbie Shaw announced over tea in the student common room. 'Barry Snowdon's on duty. There'll be standing room only in the operating theatre.'

When a horse has colic it's no joke. Abdominal pain's not funny at the best of times but for some equine patients it's the end of the road. Colic kills.

'It's a five-year-old mare. She's been seen by a vet in Hertford. He thinks she's got a twist,' Tony Regan, the houseman informed us as a battered old horsebox unloaded our patient. 'If he's right, she'll die without surgery, quick.'

The Royal Veterinary College has an equine hospital just north of London, near Potters Bar, where all the urgent cases like really bad colics go for treatment. The place is full of students, eager for experience. You spend all of your final year there. You're one step away from qualifying, so part of your training is to be on call to help the surgeons. Tonight it was my turn.

'She's in a bad way,' Barry Snowdon said once he'd completed his initial examination. 'The Hertford vet was right. It's a twist.'

Horses aren't a bit like us inside. They have a tiny stomach. Much smaller than you would ever think for an animal that size. Our caecum's almost a memory, theirs is enormous by comparison, taking up a lot of room in the abdomen. The same goes for their large intestine or colon, which is so large it has to double back and fold on itself a couple of times to fit. That's where the serious colics start. The colon fills with gas and the bowel twists on itself. If you've seen the film *Alien*, you'll have a pretty good idea of what goes on. Before you know it bits of intestine are trapped and going necrotic. Bad news.

'I'd like you to help Mr Regan perform a paracentesis,' Barry Snowdon informed me urgently. 'Be careful, mind. She's in a lot of pain and her behaviour's very unpredictable.' Horses with colic kick and roll. They're very frightened and anxious and can injure you if you're not careful.

Tony Regan and I had to insert long needles up into her abdomen to draw off fluid. The colour of the fluid would give us some idea of how the colic was progressing.

'I don't like the look of that,' Tony said as the syringe filled with ominously dark fluid. 'Normally it's clear, and you don't get much at all.'

Before you can anaesthetise a really sick horse, or

any animal come to that, you've got to make sure it can stand it. Colic makes them go into shock, and if you don't give them intravenous fluids before you operate, you might as well forget it. The shock will kill them.

'We'll keep running the intravenous fluids in through this catheter in her jugular vein until her blood gases look more promising,' Barry Snowdon told the anaesthetist. 'We won't go till she's ready. She's too acidotic at the moment.'

It took nearly an hour till Barry and Katy Cousins the anaesthetist were sure the shock of surgery wouldn't kill her.

'This abdominal fluid's getting darker by the minute,' Tony Regan shouted. 'It's now or never.'

'Right,' said Barry Snowdon. 'Scrub up, Mr Taylor. You're going to help me and Mr Regan operate.'

Great. Now was my chance to impress the great man. Not that I'd had much luck so far.

'We'll need a volunteer,' he'd said that afternoon in the obstetric department's barn, 'someone who gets on well with Friesian bulls.'

Graham Richmond gave me a shove in the back of my shoulders and pushed me to the front of the class. Amazing isn't it? You can stand at the back of a group of students, minding your own business, thinking of nothing more nor less than the nurse you met last Friday, when suddenly there you are: volunteered.

'Oh, Mr Taylor. Good,' Barry Snowdon murmured approvingly. 'We'll just see if the crash helmet fits.' One of the obstetrics technicians put the helmet on my head and tightened the chin strap. 'Perfect. Now all you need is the artificial vagina and we'll be ready for the bull. We're giving him a fertility test.'

I must have looked anxious.

'Relax. It's perfectly safe. All you have to do is whip in under him at the right moment and collect a semen sample. Nothing to it,' Barry Snowdon continued. 'Just in case there *is* a problem we'll tie a rope round your waist and tug you out of the way if things get a big dodgy.'

Arnie the massive Friesian bull was led by two technicians into the centre of the barn. There waiting for him was a teaser. I could see Arnie approved. He bellowed loudly, salivated and started pawing the ground.

Funny things bulls. You'd think nothing would turn them on more than a female cow in oestrus. But no, not a bit of it. Given the choice they're far more attracted to castrated males, or teasers. There's no accounting for taste. The teaser steer stood obliviously chomping away on some hay. He was tied securely to a post. Either side of him two great wooden ramps, to take the amorous bull's weight, were in place for Arnie's charge. It made me think that, to a bull, romance was probably a lot like ski-jumping.

'He's almost ready,' cried Barry Snowdon as the great beast grew ever more passionate. 'In you go.'

I put my head down and ran for his belly. It's one of those things that look easy in the films. Oh yes, there are films of these goings on. We'd seen plenty in the first two years of our course. A couple of the anatomy lecturers were researching into Hereford bulls and their corkscrew penises. If you ask me, it's a major surprise there are any Hereford cattle left. Most of the ones we saw wouldn't have had much luck in the great-lover stakes. They started out all right but in the excitement of it all they sort of buckled and bent and missed the point completely. Even so, white coated vets would dash in amongst them like Will Carling going for a touchdown and get their samples with ease. Show offs.

It's not a bit like that really. For one thing all the bull's grunting and groaning really puts you off. Then he gets so carried away he misses his footing once or twice on the slippery wooden ramps. My waist rope came in handy there. If Dave Bell or Graham Richmond saw me getting in trouble I suddenly found myself retreating at high speed, the artificial vagina trailing behind me. Then you've got to wait for the crucial moment. In a matter of seconds you have to steady the bull and guide the root of all his passion into this three-foot piece of rubber tubing you've been trying to attract him to. It's probably easier lassooing an Exocet.

There was a loud thwack as he bounced against the side of my crash helmet. Good job I was wearing it, or I'd have been speared right in through the ears. I was starting to panic. My hands were sweating and everything I touched seemed to be getting slippier and slippier. When suddenly – one hundred and eighty! I was there. Or rather Arnie was. The artificial vagina had done its job. I had my sample and I was hurtling backwards on the end of the rope like the space shuttle coming in for re-entry not a moment too soon. Arnie crashed off the ramps, all his passion expended. A cigarette would have been just the job but Friesians don't smoke.

'Thank you, Mr Taylor,' Barry Snowdon said, as I lay nervously exhausted on the barn floor. 'You were good. I do admire a volunteer.'

Now, as I prepared to assist at the colic operation, I had a chance to make the great man really notice me.

When the mare was safely asleep she was drawn across the theatre by a heavy duty winch and on to the huge equine operating table which then rose slowly and majestically from the floor on hydraulic legs. Most of the final year seemed to be there; if Barry Snowdon was operating, they weren't going to miss it.

'Once I've made my first incision, we'll work quickly. Clamp anything that bleeds, Mr Taylor. If there's one thing I don't care for, it's blood.'

As he worked deftly, cutting down through the layers of tissue that make up a horse's abdomen, I watched intently for the first signs of haemorrhage. If anything even thought of bleeding, I clamped it.

'We're into the abdomen. There's the twist. You can see where the colon's in trouble. Look at that black area of bowel. It's dying. It'll have to be removed.'

For a moment it seemed the whole final year was straining over my shoulder trying to get a good view. Operating *theatre*? They weren't kidding.

Tony Regan and Barry took their time to free the colon from the twist. Handling damaged bowel isn't easy. There's always a chance you're going to put your finger through it or tear it. You have to be very patient and work gently.

'We'll take out that damaged section and then perform an anastamosis to sew the healthy bits of bowel back together. How's she coping with the anaesthetic?'

Katy Cousins smiled and raised her thumb. There's always a danger that when you untwist things you release a lot of toxins into the bloodstream in a sudden rush. That can be fatal.

'More suture, Mr Taylor,' Barry Snowdon asked as he and Tony Regan began the anastamosis. 'If you see any leaks let me know.' I didn't see any leaks. There never were when Barry Snowdon operated. It always seemed to go like clockwork. Textbook stuff.

It was the same when he lectured. A green line there, a red line there, and you'd see appear on the lecture theatre blackboard a simple, informative drawing of the most complicated anatomical and surgical concept. Straight to the point, no messing. No wonder all the vets in the area sent their complicated cases to him.

One day we'd seen a horse from the King's Troop Royal Horse Artillery. They'd been rolling round Hyde Park with their guns and limbers when one of the teams of horses suddenly pulled up short. There are no brakes on the heavy artillery pieces they lug round with them and the horses had been shunted forward into each other at great speed. One had a very nasty injury to one of the tendons on a hind leg.

The army vet had given it first aid but when he realised the extent of the damage he knew that if the horse was ever going to be fit again it was a job for Barry Snowdon.

'Tendon surgery isn't easy,' he'd said as he discussed the case with us before surgery. 'Tendons have a very poor blood supply so don't heal well. I'm going to do what I can with some new carbon fibre implants to see if I can encourage healing.' Carbon fibre was a spin off from the space race. It's now used a lot in equine surgery.

Barry set to work and before long the army horse's leg looked a whole lot better. Six weeks later the injured horse was back on duty. Good as new.

Years later in that same operating theatre another army horse would receive life-saving surgery. His injuries had touched the nation. Along with several others he had been blown up by an IRA bomb. His name was Sefton.

Once the anastamosis on our present patient was complete, the colon could be placed back safely in the abdomen. The damaged, necrotic bowel was discarded and Barry, Tony and I set about repairing the incision in the horse's belly.

It always seems to take ages to stitch up after major surgery. The excitement of it all is starting to fade and stitching up seems a tiresome grind. Some sort of equine superglue would be a great help. Gradually the final year drifted away to their books or the pub and soon there were only a few of us left in the theatre with the unconscious animal. The surgery had taken over two hours.

'You stay with her till she recovers and can stand. Make sure she gets all her antibiotics and we'll give her any pain killers she might need,' Barry told me as Tony Regan and he went away to change out of their soiled surgical clothes. 'We'll be back soon and then we can all keep an eye on her.'

The first few hours are the worst. Every now and then I'd check her pulse. It was steady. She seemed much more relaxed and soon, groggily and unhurriedly, she pulled herself up to her feet.

'That's more like it,' Barry Snowdon said as he examined her later. 'You can even hear bowel sounds now. The anastamosis must be working.'

By next morning the mare was a lot better. She was starting to nibble at a bit of hay. The operation had been a success. I was shattered. But I'd been working up to asking Debbie Shaw out for weeks. I may have been wrong but I thought she'd been impressed by my work during the mare's operation the night before. It was now or never. When she came by the mare's stable, I'd ask her out.

'Sorry, Nigel, couldn't possibly manage tonight,' she said half apologetically. 'Barry Snowdon's giving a lecture on Grass Sickness to the Equine Veterinary Association, and you know I wouldn't miss that for the world. He's my hero!'

26

High summer in South Devon.

I was just sitting back on the warm, golden sand to enjoy my ice cream when I heard a dog cry out in pain. I ran across the beach and was about to examine the large, aggressive looking German Shepherd which seemed to be choking, when a loud voice behind me announced that help was at hand.

'Stand back,' he said. 'I know about all these things. I've studied first aid.'

And, with a dramatic flourish, he reached into the dog's open mouth and retrieved a rubber ball from the back of its throat. 'There you are,' he announced, while the waiting crowd applauded loudly, 'he'll be fine now. No need to worry about him.'

'Such a clever man,' the happy owner informed me as we watched our modest hero disappear amongst the tourists on the beach. 'You'd think he was a vet. He certainly knew how to treat poor Sheba.'

'Oh yes,' I agreed reluctantly. 'It just shows you how helpful first aid can be.'

I didn't think this was the time to let her know I was a qualified veterinary surgeon. I made my excuses and headed back to my half eaten ice cream. Sometimes it just isn't your day. A choc ice with heat stroke isn't much fun.

As the high speed train hurried on its way towards London that morning I began to wonder what *Tomorrow's World* would think of me. They were looking for a new presenter who had a scientific degree and who also had experience of broadcasting.

I'd never been near a television studio in my life but a degree in veterinary medicine isn't bad. And I had been appearing on local radio for a few months. 'Paws for Thought' they called my weekly vet spot. Well, at least it was a start. I don't know why I wanted to appear on television. I suppose it was a throwback to all those school plays I never got picked for. No, tell a lie, one year I was a royal guard in *The Snow Queen*. My big line was something like, 'The prisoner is here, sire.' I practised and I practised. I don't think I could have practised the soliloquy from *Hamlet* better. But as it turned out, it wasn't to be at all. Every night just as I got to my big moment the King would interrupt. 'The pris—' was about the most I ever managed. The following year I was promoted to special effects. This production had a dragon living in some deep subterranean tunnel. You didn't see him, but the audience got the general impression from the great gusts of smoke that billowed from his cave as he spoke. The trouble was we couldn't get hold of any dry ice, which is what the pop groups use to look slightly ethereal. They do this in the hope you won't notice them miming. It never works. So with no dry ice around I was asked to come up with an alternative. I was studying A-level chemistry at the time. I came up with a chemical mixture, I think it was ammonium chloride, which produced lovely damp clouds of very impressive white smoke. The first night audience thought it was great until waves of the stuff eddied off the stage and submerged the front five rows of seats. Everyone started coughing and my career in the theatre was over.

I thought *Tomorrow's World* would be great. I'd prepared my own script about how stroking dogs lowered the heart rate and helped heart attack patients recover more quickly. Very topical and I hoped highly scientific. If pushed I can be as trendy as the next man.

Suddenly there was this awful screaming in the carriage. Someone was in pain.

'Is there a doctor on the train?' the guard announced. 'We have an emergency.'

Funny, isn't it, how suddenly the whole place fills up with would-be first aiders. I looked up the coach and I could see a crowd hovering around a poor young woman who looked very uncomfortable about the whole thing. She had pretty bad abdominal pain.

'I'm a medical student. First year,' one of them told me as I went over to see if there was anything I could do. 'Trouble is we've only done the head and neck in anatomy. Below that is still a bit of a mystery to me.'

Her companion was doing his best but his medical knowledge was a bit limited too. 'I'm studying PE. I know quite a lot about pulled muscles and things, but I think this is a bit more serious, don't you?'

I told him I did and mumbled quickly that I was a veterinary surgeon as I sat down beside the lady.

'Oh, surgeon eh? Now we'll be all right.'

I gave him a reassuring smile and chatted to our patient.

'Where does it hurt, love?' I enquired softly.

She pointed to the middle of her belly. 'All over,' she said. 'It hurts like hell. And I'm not having a baby if that's what you're thinking.'

I was relieved. Animal obstetrics were one thing. I could cope with Dartmoor cattle and sheep. Somehow a packed coach on an Inter-City 125 wasn't the ideal place to start my experience of human midwifery.

'It could be your appendix. I'll get the guard to stop the train at Newbury. There's a hospital next to the station there.'

Just then a band of born-again Christians arrived. Now, I've nothing against evangelists, but there's a time and a place: this wasn't either.

'Repent ye, sayeth the Lord,' the tallest one said in an American accent. 'Prayer is the cure for all our ills.'

'Not right now,' I said. 'What she needs is a doctor, fast.'

Two sailors sitting nearby saw I was having trouble controlling the little crowd that had gathered around me and my patient. 'Me and Harry will stand in the gangway like and give you some room, mister. 'Ere, you with the bible. Hop it.'

The journey to Newbury didn't take long and soon my charge was safely unloaded by a waiting medical team. The hardest thing of all had been keeping every eager first aider from giving her cups of tea or water to make her feel better. With an imminent anaesthetic, the last thing she needed was fluids.

'Burst appendix, sir. Good job we had a surgeon like you on board,' the guard informed me at Reading. 'What kind of surgeon did you say you was? Specialist, is it?'

'Who me? Oh no, not a specialist. More a general sort of surgeon really.' I paused and hoped he wouldn't press the point. 'Yes very general. In fact about as general as you can be.'

The *Tomorrow's World* audition was great fun but not the big break I'd hoped for. I presented a complete half hour programme by myself and then sat back and waited for the verdict.

'I'm not at all sure your future lies in television,' the chief editor of the programme told me ambivalently. 'Still, there's always room for animals on the box. I mean look at *That's Life*! You never know, something might turn up.'

A few weeks later, when I'd almost forgotten about my dramatic afternoon on Mothecombe beach, I met my fearless first aider again.

'It's my bitch. She went into labour early this morning,' he announced as he lifted the smiling springer spaniel up on to the surgery table. 'I'm a bit disappointed really. Everything was going by the book, but nothing's happened for hours. No sign of any puppies.'

'By the book, eh?' I said casually. I was sure he hadn't recognised me from the beach. That would make life easier. His wife, who had come with him, added in great detail how he had avidly followed every stage of the spaniel's pregnancy with the help of a book from the library.

'Likes to keep informed, does my John. Knows a thing or two about medicine,' she told me with obvious pride.

I was beginning to wonder if first aid could be infectious.

'That's good,' I said when I examined the reluctant mother. 'Then you'll both understand when I tell you that the only way we'll deliver this litter is by Caesarean.' They listened intently as I continued. 'There's a huge puppy stuck in the birth canal. We'll have to operate.'

'That's fine,' John said excitedly. 'Would you mind if we stopped to watch? I've never seen an operation before, except on TV of course, and I'm sure we can help look after the puppies.'

I didn't really mind. It was Sunday afternoon. There was no one else about in the surgery. I could do with all the help I could get.

Once the pups were delivered, I'd be too busy dealing with mum to worry about them. John and his wife would be a great help keeping the puppies warm and making sure they were breathing correctly.

'There you are . . . sleeping like a baby,' I said as the spaniel drifted into unconsciousness. 'I'll get on with it now. I don't want to keep the pups waiting too long.'

Anaesthetising the mum always puts the pups at risk as they're anaesthetised too. The lighter and quicker the anaesthetic the better.

John watched fascinated as I prepared the bitch for surgery. He was bubbling over with enthusiasm and his excited commentary was beginning to sound like a David Coleman effort on *Match of the Day*.

'That's the antiseptic going in. Keeps the germs out, you know,' he informed us breathlessly. 'And yes, yes, he's about to make his first incision . . . Wait for it. Wait for it. Yes, here it comes. Here comes some,' there was an unexpected pause, 'some blood.'

What can you do if someone decides to faint in the middle of an operation? My first concern was my anaesthetised patient.

'What you going to do about John?' his wife asked without too much concern.

She was very pretty and I'd have been a fool not to try the kiss of life if she'd collapsed. But John, well.

'Not a lot. Now that the surgery's quiet again we'll leave him where he is. Your spaniel needs a bit of peace.'

'Fair enough,' she said and smiled. 'He does go on a bit.'

The operation was a complete success and John's spaniel gave birth to seven lovely puppies. All very healthy. It took them a while to wake up from the anaesthetic but soon they were squeaking and squawking like all new born pups. I'd almost forgotten about John when I heard an indistinct mumbling in the background.

'What happened?' he murmured as he staggered to his feet.

'Oh, nothing much. You fainted when you saw blood. Happens all the time. If people can breathe easily I leave them where they are. They soon come round. Just like it says in the books.'

27

Bonfire night in Plympton must be a bit like living on the 'peace' line in downtown Beirut. If you like explosions and loud bangs it's just the place for you. For me and most of the animals I look after, it's a pain.

'Sheba doesn't like these fireworks you know, Mr Taylor. Scare her rigid they do,' Mrs Lubbock informed me the next morning. 'Poor little cat. She spent all last night hiding under my bed. And just look at her skin.'

Oh dear. Mrs Lubbock. I try my best to get on with all my clients but there are some I just don't see eye to eye with, and probably never will. Mrs Lubbock is one of them.

It's been the same for years. I tell Mrs Lubbock Sheba has cat flu. She doesn't believe me.

'I have a friend who tells me all tortoiseshells are asthmatic. She's a cat breeder. She knows what she's talking about. Flu, indeed.'

So, never one to disagree with expert knowledge, I treat Sheba for asthma. I use the same antibiotics and mucolytics I would have used to treat her flu, and amazingly she gets better.

'There, Mr Taylor. Her asthma's a lot better now. Marvellous what the right treatment will do, isn't it?'

'Oh absolutely. Absolutely, Mrs Lubbock,' I say enthusiastically. 'I couldn't agree more. That's the marvellous thing about this job you know. You learn a little more every day.'

When Sheba caught ringworm, I thought Mrs Lubbock and I were going to come to blows.

'You are telling me my cat has got ringworm? That's not very nice, is it. My friend who breeds cats has had a look at her and says it definitely isn't ringworm.'

'But can't you see how those patches of skin fluoresce bright green when I shine an ultraviolet light on them? That's a pretty good diagnostic test for ringworm.' Sheba's skin was all lit up. False teeth at a disco couldn't have shone brighter.

'Never,' Mrs Lubbock insisted. 'She must have got something on her coat. Nail varnish or something, I don't know. It isn't ringworm.'

Ringworm is a fungus. Cats and dogs get it, so do cattle and horses. Cow ringworm is pretty unpleasant. If you're unlucky enough to catch it it can cause some very nasty sores. Over the years I've often diagnosed it in people, especially children, as well as their pets. One little girl had a very sore bald patch right in the middle of her beautiful long dark hair. She'd come with her mum and the family cat to be checked because one of the doctors at our local health centre thought the cat might be the source of the problem. The cat was clear. No skin disease anywhere. But

Tracy's head erupted in a bright green glow under the ultraviolet. Ringworm, caught from her uncle's cows. She'd been visiting his smallholding and scraped her head on some fencing they'd been rubbing up against. Just as well it wasn't the cat; some parents panic when they're told the family pet has ringworm. They won't have it treated so the poor creature gets put to sleep. Sometimes a lot depends on an accurate diagnosis.

'Sheba has ringworm, Mrs Lubbock. No doubt about it. She'll need treatment.'

'I will not have my cat treated for ringworm, Mr Taylor, and that's final. I don't care what you say.'

'Very well then, why don't I treat Sheba for dermatitis? Fungal dermatitis. And let's see if she improves.'

'Oh yes, that sounds much better. Dermatitis, that's more like it. That's what my friend thought it might be.'

'Fine, we'll try some Griseofulvin. That usually works well for fungal dermatitis.'

It usually works brilliantly for ringworm too. Not surprising really. That's what it's designed to cure.

'You're the expert, Mr Taylor. Whatever you suggest!'

Today though, Sheba was in a sorry state. Large patches of her skin were very red and inflamed. Huge chunks of her coat were falling out. You could feel scabs all along her back, round her neck and over the base of her tail. Mrs Lubbock was rightly worried.

'It's miliary eczema,' I said authoritatively. 'The

Americans call it "scabby cat disease", which is a great name and descriptive too. It's a type of allergy.'

'What's she allergic to, Mr Taylor?' Mrs Lubbock enquired concernedly. 'I hope it's nothing in the house. I'm very fussy, you know.'

How could I tell her it was fleas? People react very differently when you tell them their pet has a flea related illness. Usually it's badly. No one likes the thought of uninvited visitors taking over the living room. But there you are, if you have a pet, expect fleas and just take steps to deal with them.

Mind you, I'm not at all sure these days if fleas are the only cause of miliary eczema in cats. I made the mistake of going to a lecture in London at one of the big veterinary congresses some years ago and my approach to dermatology has never been quite the same since.

Danny Scott, the world famous veterinary dermatologist from Cornell, was giving a paper on scabby cat disease and other common cat skin problems. He told us how he travelled all over the States convincing vets the cause was fleas. Fine, until he reached Alaska. There he was interrupted in mid-lecture by a polite but unimpressed practising vet who told him, 'In Fairbanks we got scabby cats a-plenty, but in Fairbanks we ain't got no fleas.' Fleas don't like Alaska. I can't say I blame them.

Fleas love South Devon though, so I was sure Sheba's miliary eczema was probably flea related. I was just steeling myself for the inevitable conflict when I told Mrs Lubbock this when she suddenly interrupted me.

'I don't know how you do it, Mr Taylor. You must be a genius,' she said, and turned to her husband Stan who used to join her at the surgery from time to time. I got the impression he was a reluctant pet lover. 'It's just like I said, Stan. It's those ruddy soldiers with their horrible guns. I knew it.'

Mrs Lubbock had just moved to a new house outside Bickleigh where the Royal Marines have their barracks and their firing range. The Marines don't bother many people but, it seemed, they did upset Mrs Lubbock, and worse, now it seemed they were affecting Sheba.

'Every time they fire their guns, Sheba comes out in this rash. You won't believe it Stan, but Sheba's allergic to them. That's what she is allergic to. Mr Taylor knew. *Military eczemer*, that's it.'

Who am I to blow against the wind? If Mrs Lubbock thought it was *military eczemer*, it was *military eczemer*.

I began to explain the treatment Sheba needed. 'It's quite simple really. All we do is put Sheba on the pill.'

Stan smiled broadly, but his wife didn't. She glared alarmingly at me.

'But, Mr Taylor, my Sheba doesn't need the pill. She's been neutralised. You don't pay vets good money to have your cat neutralised and then find they have to go on the pill. It's not on.'

I thought that perhaps if I explained how the treatment worked she might be more amenable.

'Look, there's lots of reasons why cats get miliary eczema but one thing's for sure, drugs called steroids control it. The pill's converted by the liver to a very effective steroid. It doesn't affect her sex life at all but it will cure her skin problem.'

'I don't know what you're suggesting,' Mrs Lubbock replied. 'Sheba's a most respectable cat. She wouldn't need the pill at all if it wasn't for the Marines.'

Stan gave me a knowing look. 'Now where have I heard that before?' he said with a broad grin.

Luckily I convinced Mrs Lubbock that with the proper treatment Sheba would soon get better and, over the next few weeks, she did. Her coat soon looked glossy and full of health once again. But Mrs Lubbock still stayed as irascible and hard to please as ever.

One morning she was in a pretty belligerent mood. Sheba had an ear infection.

'No, it couldn't possibly be caused by ear mites!'

I tried to keep calm but it was pretty obvious to Lorna, my nurse, that I was rapidly losing my cool.

I left Mrs Lubbock in the consulting room and went for a breather in the dispensary. 'God, if only I had a banger or something I'd bung it at her and shift her out of here that way.'

'You can't do that,' Lorna said emphatically. 'Sheba doesn't like loud bangs. You might start her skin allergy off again!'

28

My friend Ernie was really enjoying his weekend with me in Cornwall. It's not exactly the wild and woolly west down round Liskeard but riding shotgun with a country vet was nearly as exciting as Wells Fargo.

We'd lost count of all the farms we'd been to and the animals we'd had to care for. The country life so different from his city home back in Plymouth suited him perfectly. When he set eyes on the pig he was delighted.

'Big and smelly. That's how I like 'em. There's something comical about a pig,' he continued enthusiastically. 'Real comedians, pigs. Ain't she a beauty?'

She certainly was. In fact I don't think I've ever seen a bigger, smellier pig. It wasn't going to be too long before she was a mum and in her advanced state of pregnancy she looked all the world like a huge, stranded, pink whale.

A couple of weekends later I was just settling down to read the Sunday papers when the phone rang.

'Nelson Pascoe, Menheniot, here. That big pig of mine, she's started to farrow. Nothing's happened for ages now. I think you ought to come and see her.'

Ernie's pig. Normally pigs pop out their piglets

without much difficulty. Blink and you miss it. Ernie's pig couldn't have taken her natural childbirth classes seriously. She was in trouble. If I didn't help her soon I might lose the whole litter.

I was a little surprised to see Nelson wearing a suit when I called at his farm. I'd never thought of Nelson as a follower of fashion but perhaps Jeff Banks and the *Clothes Show* were making more of an impression than I imagined. When he jumped in my car and told me to drive to the little chapel on the edge of his land, my curiosity increased. The whole village seemed to be assembled in the chapel and I felt a little out of place as he ushered me through the main door and down the aisle.

There are lots of these little chapels dotted all over Cornwall. Loads have been converted into holiday homes which in some ways is a real shame. Nelson and the village had looked after this one, though, and still held regular services. There at the back of the organ in a small room was Ernie's pig. One thing was sure, she wasn't wearing the latest perfume. Pig BO is pretty overpowering, especially when they've been living in a confined space.

'It's no good. I can't move her,' Nelson explained anxiously holding a hankie over his nose and mouth. 'She came in here about a week ago. You know pigs. Anywhere dry and warm and they're in like a shot.'

Outside in the chapel, the congregation were getting restless. All this veterinary excitement together with the heady aroma of moist, expectant pig was more than they'd bargained for. And today was a special occasion.

'It would happen now,' said Nelson. 'The chapel's built on the site of one of John Wesley's meetings. You remember he rode all over Cornwall preaching at places like Gwennap pit and here, in Menheniot. And today we've got a big noise coming down from Central Hall. He's giving sermons at all the places Wesley visited.'

Nelson looked anxiously at his watch.

'I'm sorry, the service is about to start and I'll have to go. After all, it was me who invited him here in the first place.' With that he was gone and Ernie's pig and I were left exchanging suspicious glances at each other in the darkened box room.

I'm quite used to being left on my own with expectant animals and being told to get on with it. Once I was left delivering a litter of Cavalier King Charles spaniels in a breeder's back bedroom. She was busy arranging for an undertaker to come and take away her poor grandmother who had died in the night. The trouble was, grannie hadn't been moved and lay in her final repose under a sheet on the bed right above where the Cavalier was whelping.

'You don't mind, do you? Only, Lucy won't go anywhere else to whelp. She always loved being near gran,' the tearful lady explained. 'I won't be long.'

She was ages. Lucy and I settled down for a long session. I gave her some oxytocin and some calcium by injection to help things along, and then waited for the pups.

They took their time. Of course it didn't help that every now and then Lucy and I were disturbed by a deep rumbling followed by a large belch and a fart. Grannie was at peace but her bowels weren't. At every fart, the dog would stop and look accusingly at me. I would point to the bedsheets and Lucy would go back to her labour. By the time the undertaker arrived we had six pups. I was glad. I couldn't take any more. Grannie gave one last beauty as I packed up my medical bag. The undertaker paused, wrinkled up his nose and looked directly at me.

To begin with Ernie's pig was quite placid and didn't even murmur as I gently examined her. A piglet was lodged in the birth canal and he'd have to be moved. Using plenty of soap and water, I worked him free. It didn't take long, but the sow didn't like it.

The congregation were singing 'All creatures that on Earth do dwell' at full voice, which was just as well really as her squeals would have put the fear of God into them. Once the first piglet was free she settled down and it wasn't long before the rest of the family put in an appearance. I gave her an injection of pituitary extract to speed things up and sat back and relaxed. It was my big mistake. For some reason as her family got bigger the more she disliked me. Animal behaviourists would probably have a fancy name for it but whatever the reason she was getting pretty foul tempered.

She was making the most awful snorting and grunting sounds and each time she popped out a piglet her squeals reached a fearsome crescendo, like a soul in

187

torment. It was pretty obvious she was going to make a dive for me any minute if I didn't get out of the way soon.

The organist had obviously heard the sow protesting and played ever louder in a frantic attempt at musical one-upmanship. The congregation were having difficulty following the tune as he struggled to conceal the squeals coming from below. Suddenly, all became ominously quiet. The guest preacher was just beginning his sermon and had just reached a bit about 'driving the sinners out of the Kingdom of Heaven', when the sow attacked. With a frenzied gnashing of her teeth she came straight for me. In an instant I burst out through the door of the box room and fled as fast as my legs would take me. It was too much for the assembled villagers. I almost thought they were going to break into applause at the sight of their vet hurtling down the aisle hotly pursued by an angry pig. *Songs of Praise* would have loved it.

I don't know what John Wesley would have thought. He was quite fond of pigs. But Nelson Pascoe didn't appreciate it, I could tell.

The next time I took Ernie to Nelson's farm he glared at him angrily. 'Aren't you the fellow who made such a fuss of my blessed pig?'

'Not really,' said Ernie. 'In fact I'm more of a budgie man. You always know where you are with a budgie. More than you can say about pigs. Unreliable buggers, pigs. They always let you down at the last minute.'

I had to agree. I've never been let down by a budgie yet.

29

'Don't worry, you won't be busy. Nothing ever happens. Mr Vernon says you can depend upon it.'

Archie Vernon was always going to the dogs. Flashford Greyhound stadium. Somewhere south of the River Thames. Three nights a week. Tonight was my first time.

'It's so quiet, he always brings his tape recorder and headphones. He's been studying O-level German. Last year he did Portuguese and Spanish,' the receptionist had said to me before I drove out across South London to Flashford.

Riveting stuff. Still, I suppose if you've only been a vet for five days it doesn't pay to go in search of too much drama. A quiet time sounded just perfect.

I'd heard about these greyhound stadiums. The vet had to check the dogs before each race and then watch them as they hurtled round the course after the electric hare. There was always a chance one would get tangled up with it and get injured. You had to be on the lookout for the dog that had been got at, too. Give a greyhound a nice heavy meal before he races and he's done for. Then there's the old 'squeeze them in the balls' trick as you put them in the starting traps. A quick caress from the kennel boy or girl at the right moment and the last thing they worried about was being first past the finishing post. No, you had to keep your eyes open if you were working at a greyhound track, but Archie Vernon didn't seem too bothered by it all. Then again, Flashford to him was a sort of Open University. He'd be too busy studying to be bothered by anything that happened on the track.

At first he didn't hear me as I hammered on his car window. His headphones were clamped securely over his ears and he was studying the *Veterinary Record* as I've never seen anybody study the *Veterinary Record* before. I guessed that he'd had enough of foreign languages. The Royal College were keen for all vets to study and improve themselves; perhaps Archie had seen the light and caught the specialisation bug. Mind you, not that I've ever found the *Record* that fascinating. It's great if you're looking for a job. Loads of adverts from vets seeking assistants and the occasional 'young lady seeks interesting position with veterinary surgeon in the countryside' from a would-be nurse. At least that's what I've always assumed. Then there are always lots of clinical papers. Foot and mouth in the Indian Elephant, Reproductive failure in the Zebra. Just the sort of information the average vet like me needs at his fingertips. No, I couldn't understand how Archie Vernon found the *Veterinary Record* so all-absorbing.

I crouched nearer the car window till I was looking right over his shoulder. There, tucked in the centre pages was the sort of magazine you normally have to reach up to the top shelf in newsagents for. *Big and Bouncy*, the lurid title screamed. It wasn't the kind of continuous education the Royal College were after, I'm sure, but I bet it livened up Archie's *Vet Record*. Slowly he realised he was being watched but not before I'd got a good glimpse of the 'readers problems' he was so engrossed in.

Archie nearly strangled himself with his headphones as he struggled to wind down his window. He seemed pretty flustered.

'I was just catching up with this week's *Veterinary Record*,' he said awkwardly. 'There's always something you can learn from it.'

'So I see,' I said, trying to keep a straight face. 'It's a lot more interesting than it used to be.'

I introduced myself.

'I'm Nigel Taylor. I answered your advert for a locum. Tell me what I have to do.'

You never know what you're letting yourself in for when you're a locum. You take over somebody's practice at short notice. If you're lucky they've got all the equipment you need. If not, you just get on with it.

Once, in one of the London practices, I started work one Monday. My first job was to spey a Jack Russell terrier. No problem. Except that there wasn't an anaesthetic machine in the place and as soon as I gave the dog an intravenous injection the nurse, a multi-coloured punk rocker, fell to the floor.

'I fainted, man. Right out. You know how it is,' wasn't much use to me but there you are, locums just get on with it. Nurse or no nurse, the dog had to be operated on. The first thing I did when I opened my own practice years later was to buy all those pieces of equipment I missed when I was a locum. I couldn't afford them but I didn't care. I'd known the reality of making do and for me and my patients it just wasn't on.

Some vets I worked for could be very unpredictable. Once I lived in a vet's house near Ipswich while I looked after his practice. He didn't trust locums one bit. He'd even removed the needle from his record player to make sure I didn't play a single record while he was away on holiday. I've never been so quiet in my life. As he didn't trust anyone but himself to operate he made sure I had no operations to do. In fact there was nothing to do. Except one day when I came close to a cystotomy. I took its stitches out. Soon I was getting calls from the other vets in the town.

'Watch him, the day he comes back off holiday he'll pick an argument with you and then refuse to pay your locum fee,' one told me late one evening.

'But why? I've done nothing wrong. I've not seen any patients. It's really boring here.'

'All the locums say the same. I don't know how he makes any money. But he's a funny bugger. Watch out.'

I didn't know whether to believe him but when Colin Stuart, who'd been a year above me at college, rang I knew he wasn't having me on.

'That sod refused to pay me. Said I hadn't turned out for a visit one night. I had awful trouble getting any money out of him. In fact I left a Barbour jacket there. I'm sure he lifted it off me. I couldn't find it anywhere.'

'I'll get the nurse to look for it. Thanks for the warning, Colin. I'll watch it.'

Sure enough when Saturday came my employer picked a quarrel with me.

'Sandra says you've not been taking the phones at night. Leaving them off the hook. That's what she said.'

It was pointless arguing. All week Sandra, the nurse, had told me he'd say that. It was one of his favourite lines.

'Could I have my wages please?' I asked quietly.

'Certainly not. I'll think about it today. You've got one more night to be on call here. My wife and I are going out at seven. I'll think about it then.'

Seven o'clock came and a cheque was thrust at me.

'There you are. I can't say you deserve it. Make sure you answer all the calls tonight.'

There weren't any. There never were.

Next morning I waited with my suitcase packed till first light. Then as silently as I could I tiptoed down the stairs and out into the fresh Suffolk air. I was going home. I was never going to do a locum again. Till the next time.

So here I was at the dog track making myself known to Archie Vernon. As we talked the tannoy belched out an announcement.

'Would the duty veterinary surgeon come to the steward's office at once, please.'

'You're on, mate. Good luck,' shouted Archie Vernon as he pulled away in his car. 'Remember you're the vet. Whatever you say goes. And don't look so worried. Nothing ever happens.'

The steward was keen to get on with the pre-race checks.

'No Mr Vernon tonight, then. Studying I expect. I've never known a man study so much. Always got his nose buried in a book. Still, I'm sure you'll do.'

He led me to the kennels. The dogs who would be racing tonight were led before me. I checked their documents and gave them a thorough examination. No problems. Perhaps Archie Vernon was right after all.

'That's it, then. Now you watch the races. We'll shout if we need you,' the steward said, and disappeared off to his duties.

The first two races were over in a flash. Released from the traps the greyhounds zipped past me like greased lightning. There was no doubt about it, these were very fit dogs. I wouldn't be needed at all. Great. I could start to relax. I went to one of the bars around the course and bought a drink. The third race was about to start and I thought I'd watch it in style. I saw the bookies hard at work and was tempted for a minute to put a few pennies on number four, but I didn't think it was the done thing for the vet on call. No, I'd just watch this one.

It was a hurdle race. The greyhounds launched

themselves around the track again, only this time every few yards they had to jump a hurdle. They didn't seem to notice. They were moving almost as fast as when they were on the flat. All, that is, except number four. Third hurdle out he took a tumble and rolled about on the track in pain. Crikey, this was it. I'd better do something. I ran across to him. His kennel girl was already there.

'He landed awkward like, mister. I think he's torn a ligament or something,' she informed me.

'Yes, yes,' I mumbled. 'Could be, but if he can't put his leg to the floor we'll have to get some X-rays just in case.'

Greyhounds are great actors. I guess they watch too much football on the television. Anyway, it seemed that within minutes of his apparently dreadful fall he was up and trotting again as if nothing had happened. Great. I was relieved.

My relief didn't last long. Suddenly there was an awful commotion at the finishing line.

'It's number six, she's dead,' someone cried.

'What?' I shouted. 'How the hell did that happen?'

Trainers appeared from nowhere.

'What was it, mate? Heart attack?'

'Drugs, then, was that it? Was she nobbled?'

How on earth did I know? I hadn't even seen her die. Apparently number six had completed the race and suddenly dropped just like a stone as she crossed the finishing line. Archie Vernon would be amused. Fifteen years, nothing happens. Then this, and I miss it.

'Would the veterinary surgeon come to the steward's office?' It was the tannoy again. 'The veterinary surgeon is needed urgently.'

A posse of anxious greyhound trainers followed me as I ran for the steward's office.

'What are you going to do?' the steward said menacingly. 'I'd get that dog away from here if I was you. There's all sorts of nasty rumours flying about. People are getting upset, if you get my drift.'

I got his drift. I found the dog's owner and bundled its body into the boot of my car.

'A post-mortem. That's what we need, a post-mortem. Probably a heart attack,' I said reassuringly. I drove away from Flashford as fast as I could.

It was a heart attack all right. You'd think a trained athlete of a dog like a greyhound could cope with a quick sprint over the hurdles. But not number six, not that night. And I had to be there.

The whole thing gave Archie Vernon his best laugh in years. 'I can't understand it. Flashford's usually so boring. I don't suppose you'll want to go back again tonight.'

'Not if I can avoid it,' I said hopefully. 'If it's OK with you I'll stay in tonight and go over some of my college notes. I'm seeing so many new things being in practice I need to read up on a lot of them.'

'Oh I know,' he said, 'you've got to keep up to date, even if you've been in practice as long as I have.'

He paused and then with a mischievous grin he added, 'Want to borrow this week's *Veterinary Record*? It's a beauty.'

30

'I've never seen an animal in so much pain.' Janice's voice rose alarmingly as we watched the heavy mare stumble and fall to the stable floor. 'Poor girl, do you think we can help her? She looks really ill to me.'

Frank Bryant was worried too. Cherry was his favourite mare. He was hoping she'd have a foal this year. He hadn't expected any problems.

I like shire horses. Gentle giants. Not so long ago they worked on all the farms round here but now they're mostly kept as pets. The farmers, like Frank, will tell you they're all kept for showing and breeding, 'got to earn their keep, Mr Taylor'. But I've seen him late at night in the stable talking to Cherry and the others like they were giant puppies. He loves them.

'She's due any day now. I thought she'd started, but there's no sign of a foal. Just this rotten colic. It's got a lot worse since I rang you,' he explained dejectedly. 'I couldn't get near her twenty minutes ago. She was like a thing possessed. Thank goodness she's quieter now.'

I knew just what he meant. Once when I was in the Highlands I'd been called to see a Clydesdale mare in trouble on Lord Bugdale's estate not far from Dornoch. She'd lashed out at a gate and somehow got one of her hind legs tangled up between the bars. She was going frantic and the gate was wrenched off its hinges and was scything the air like a lethal weapon. Gradually we calmed her and I was able to give her a sedative before we gently sawed the bars of the gate and released her. Lord Bugdale was delighted. 'I thought we'd have to shoot her, young man,' he said. 'But that sedative worked a treat. Well done.'

To look at him you'd think Lord Bugdale had stepped straight out of the world of Bertie Wooster. Plus fours, a monocle and a tweed hat. And the roundest, happiest face I've ever seen. He liked people and people liked him. Especially the vet Anthony Hadrian's daughter Naomi, who was then about five. She used to come up to Lord Bugdale's estate often with her dad. Everywhere he went people greeted the smiling old aristocrat with 'Yes, m'lord', 'No, m'lord'. It was too much for Naomi. As they sat down for tea in the main hall of Lord Bugdale's castle, his favourite afternoon treat for little girls and hungry veterinary surgeons, she suddenly looked up and questioned her father.

'Daddy, why does everyone keep calling him My Lord?' And then she added in a hushed voice, 'Is he God?'

Mind you, it wouldn't surprise me one bit if God turned out to be a lot like Lord Bugdale. I hope he is.

I was pleased Cherry was a little quieter. With luck she'd tired herself out. I didn't fancy trying to examine her as she threw herself around the stable. It's always a little tricky working behind a mare's back legs, and, with Cherry's violent behaviour it wasn't just tricky. If you didn't have a crash helmet, it could be suicidal.

'I can't feel the foal at all,' I announced as I reached gently up into the dilated birth canal. I was lucky. Cherry was so exhausted she just lay there sighing loudly as I completed my examination. 'It's got me baffled. My hand goes in so far, then there's a tight band. It's like hitting a brick wall.'

Janice had watched my delicate probings with interest. As a midwife she'd delivered hundreds of babies at the busy Exeter Hospital. I'd known her for years. One afternoon over coffee at Hanson's on the Cathedral Green, she'd asked if she could come out on my rounds to see some farmyard confinements. Windwhistle farm was her first. I'd often seen Frank leading the shires through Hemerdon village early on summer evenings, and I'd stop the car and just sit and watch as the beautiful animals sauntered by. Cherry was the loveliest and usually she had no trouble foaling. They just popped out before you knew it. But today, things were more exciting than Janice and I bargained for.

'Sounds like a uterine twist to me,' she said. 'Just like it says in that veterinary obstetric book you lent me. Because the womb's twisted up on itself, you can't get through to feel the foal.'

That was it. Just before they're born foals sort themselves out so they can be born the right way round, head first. But if they move a little too vigorously, the mare's womb twists and the foal's stuck.

'What can you do now?' Frank asked after I explained Cherry's predicament. 'We're going to lose them both, aren't we?'

'Not if I can sort this twist out, Frank,' I replied with confidence. I didn't like to tell him I'd only ever seen a twist once before – in Canada – and then we'd had to operate to save the mare. The foal had died. 'But I'll need the biggest plank you can find and the fattest farm lad you've got.'

Frank and Janice seemed a little puzzled at these strange requests, but there was no time to explain. First we had to anaesthetise Cherry. I gave her as low a dose of barbiturate as possible. I wanted to save the foal, so I couldn't afford to give her too much. Anything you give the mother goes straight to the womb and puts the unborn foal at risk.

'Right, now she's asleep, Janice, we lay the plank across her belly. If you and Frank's lad stand on it you'll hold the foal in place. Frank and I will turn Cherry over. If we're lucky, we'll be able to untwist the womb and then we can get at the foal.'

The twist was taking a clockwise turn so I figured if we turned Cherry over from her right side to her left while the foal was held still by Janice's plank we'd be all set for a normal foaling.

Frank and I struggled to turn Cherry over. It didn't work first time but gradually as we stuck at it and repeated our attempts to help her, I could feel the foal's head freeing itself. Our plan had worked. The twist unravelled and we could deliver the foal.

'Can I help?' Janice said as I attached the foaling ropes to the youngster's forelegs.

'The quicker we get him out the better. He's still breathing.'

Working as a team we soon got the foal out and as he lay gasping for breath on the stable floor, we thought we might have won. From now on, he was on his own.

'It's a good job it wasn't twins,' Janice exclaimed as the foal gradually pulled himself up to stand. 'He's enormous. No wonder mum was in trouble.'

'Luckily twins are rare, Janice,' I said, 'although now we're using ultrasound to scan a lot of our expectant mums you'd be surprised how many equine pregnancies start off as twins. One just dies off early, that's all. It's as if nature knows one foal is plenty for any mare.'

'Or any midwife,' she said wearily.

It didn't take long for Cherry to recover from her ordeal and 'Hanson', Janice's name for her brave foal, seemed none the worse for his unexpected adventure.

'I don't suppose you'll be charging much for this visit,' Frank said as we climbed into the car ready to leave the farm. 'I mean your friend there, the midwife, she'll be on the National Health won't she?'

31

Sometimes you get an offer you just can't refuse.

'Would you like to meet the future? Her name's ELISA.' Ian Lawson unpacked a little foil package and pulled out what looked to me like a tiny white egg cup. 'Enzyme Linked Immunosorbent Assay. It's the way all diagnosis is going to go,' he continued enthusiastically, holding up the 'egg cup' for me to see. 'All you need is some blood. Mix it with some reagents. Pour it in and in less than ten minutes it can tell you if that sick cat you're looking after has got feline leukaemia or FIV.'

I'd heard of feline leukaemia but FIV was a new one on me.

'Feline Immunodeficiency Virus. It's part of the same family of viruses as AIDS.'

'I'm not sure I like the sound of that.'

'Don't worry,' Ian said reassuringly, 'luckily for you and me there's no way you and I can catch any sort of AIDS from cats. It's just not transmissible.'

'Glad to hear it,' I said, relieved. 'If this diagnostic test kit is as good as you say then it's going to be a great help to any vet treating cats.'

'It's better than that,' Ian continued. 'The biotechnology company I work for has already developed ELISA kits for canine parvovirus and we're working on distemper, hepatitis and all the rest. One day you'll know in minutes exactly what's wrong with all your patients. Marvellous.'

I've often wondered what it must have been like being a vet before anyone discovered antibiotics. I'm sure people coped but sometimes it must have been awful just watching animals with infections die when you knew no matter how good a veterinary surgeon you were, you could never get them better. When the first antibiotics like penicillin and the sulphonamides arrived I bet all the vets then thought it was nothing short of a miracle.

Not that the new wonder drugs were the answer to everything. There were still the viral illnesses that caused major epidemics of animal disease and could kill healthy pets in a matter of days. I can remember a young rough collie puppy my mum and dad bought for me and my sister when we lost Rusty. The poor soul died in agony a few weeks later. Distemper. There was lots of it about. No one had a vaccine against it. Some dogs survived the initial infection but were often ill for the rest of their lives. Our tiny puppy screamed and screamed and couldn't stop having fits. If I close my eyes I can see and hear her now. We would have done anything to help her. She died before the vet arrived.

For a few years it must have seemed that veterinary research had gone into overdrive. A vaccine against distemper was developed and soon marvellous new vaccines arrived to protect cats and dogs against all the major common viruses that affect them. Now, of course, owners take it all for granted. That tiny injection their pet gets once a year or so doesn't look much, and so some people don't bother at all. But they've never seen sick animals die unnecessarily when they could have easily been protected.

There are some viruses that still cause us problems, especially some of the cat ones, but as Ian Lawson's new diagnostic test kit proved, we're getting there.

'Tommy's not well, Mr Taylor. His eyes look really sore and he's not been eating at all for the past week or so,' Mrs Woodford told me as she put the tattered old cardboard cat box on the consulting table. 'I don't think he can see.' Mrs Woodford has been rescuing cats for years. If there's a stray run over or a kitten with no home to go to they all end up with her.

'If they need a home, they've got one, young man,' she'd told me when we first met. 'I like cats, and do you know I'm sure they like me.'

I'm sure they did, too. You can't manage an awful lot on a pension these days but Mrs Woodford's cats have never gone without. I'd often call by and find her munching her way through a couple of soggy old cream crackers and not much else whilst all around the cats would be tucking into the day's tasty treat. Boiled cod, tinned tuna or whatever Mrs Woodford could afford.

'You spoil these cats,' I'd say cheekily.

'Not at all.' Always the same reply. 'As long as they're happy, so am I.'

Tommy was one of her pensioners. He'd turned up on her doorstep years ago and, probably realising he was on to a very good thing, had never left. In his day the ginger cat must have been a beauty but today he looked tired and dejected. His left eye seemed painful and he was squinting as I shone the light of the opthalmoscope into it.

'He's got an iritis. His iris is very inflamed. If you look closely you can see how sore it is, there right in the middle of the eye.'

Mrs Woodford peered closely at the elderly cat's face. 'Oh yes, I can see what you mean. Is there something seriously wrong with him?'

'Well,' I said, 'I can't be sure but as he has a very high temperature too there's a good chance he's got feline infectious peritonitis or FIP.'

I explained to her how FIP was caused by a virus and how usually it caused a lot of fluid to build up in the abdomen. But sometimes the virus affects other parts of the body like the kidneys or the eye. That's not so easy to diagnose.

'I can't afford any expensive blood tests,' she said when I told her I could send a blood sample to Glasgow Veterinary School to make sure of my diagnosis. 'Isn't there anything else you can do?'

'I can try him on some antibiotic injections and eye drops for a few days just in case I'm wrong. Chloramphenicol sometimes brings temperatures down and it's good for eye infections too. If Tommy gets better I'm wrong.'

But Tommy didn't get better. As the days went by he got a lot worse. His eye became ever sorer and no matter what I did his temperature wouldn't drop. It was FIP for sure.

'You can put him to sleep, Mr Taylor, but I'll give him one more cuddle as he goes. He can die in my arms.'

Sometimes I hate being a vet. You can tell the owners all about their pet's illness. What sort of virus sub-particle causes the trouble and a hundred and one other interesting and informative things about the disease. But with something like FIP the one thing you can't do is offer them any hope of treatment. There isn't any. You might as well have both your hands tied behind your back.

I had to hope none of the other cats would catch it. The textbooks were on my side. FIP is pretty wide-spread in the cat population but very few go on to develop the full clinical disease. I just had to cross my fingers and hope the rest of Mrs Woodford's chums would be all right.

When Sam and Chloe fell ill a few months later I thought, this is it, we're going to lose the lot.

It wasn't FIP this time.

'Sam's been listless for a while now,' Mrs Woodford informed me one afternoon during surgery, 'and I could be wrong but there's a big swelling in his belly.'

There was. A huge mass like a swollen orange sat where one of his kidneys should be.

206

'Looks like a lymphosarcoma,' I said sadly. 'He's got no future, I'm afraid. I could do some X-rays but really just feeling his abdomen has told me all I need to know. He'll have to be put to sleep. What's wrong with Chloe?'

'She keeps sneezing all the time, Mr Taylor, like she's got a really bad cat flu. And look at her gums. They're raw, red raw.'

The tortoiseshell cat sat on the table snuffling and sneezing. She seemed pretty miserable. I didn't like the look of this. I began to wonder if both these cats might have feline leukaemia or FIV. Where you got one you often got the other. Both viruses depressed cats' immune systems so much it left them wide open to all sorts of infections. Feline leukaemia often caused tumours like lymphosarcoma.

'I think we should blood test Sam and Chloe and all the others. You might have some very nasty viruses just waiting to make all your cats ill.'

'But Mr Taylor, I've told you before, I can't afford any blood tests. What can I do?'

That night I rang Ian Lawson. Sometimes when something new hits the veterinary market if you're very lucky they'll let you have some to try.

'Look, Ian,' I explained, 'I've got a dozen cats to blood test. My client hasn't got a bean. Any chance we could have some of the diagnostic kits as a bit of a trial? She'd be ever so grateful, and so would I.'

There was a pause.

'Why not? I'm sure we can spare a few. If it's a success you'll tell all the vets in town, won't you.'

'Ian, I'll even wear one of your T-shirts out jogging. Anything to help her.'

'Right mate, you're on. I'll be in Plymouth next week. I'll come and give you a hand.'

Luckily you didn't need much blood for one of Ian's tests. Cats aren't the best blood donors in the world.

'There love, see? It only takes a few minutes,' he told Mrs Woodford as he started to test the samples. 'Then we'll know for sure who's carrying these viruses and who isn't. A simple colour change from white to blue is all we're looking for.' He held one of his magic 'egg cups' up for Mrs Woodford to inspect. 'Simple, isn't it?'

'If you say so, dear,' Mrs Woodford said resignedly.

Chloe was positive. So were three of the others, Sally, Twinkle and Pumpkin. They all had feline leukaemia and FIV.

'What are you going to do now?' Ian asked me once we knew the results. 'I don't think she's the sort of lady who'll want any put down. Anyway, you've got to test them again in three months to be sure. She'll have to isolate Chloe and the other positives.'

And that's what Mrs Woodford did. One of her neighbours built her an outside pen and put a cat-house in it. Chloe and her three pals lived there happily, while the other cats took over Mrs Woodford's downstairs just like they've always done.

'As long as she doesn't become too ill, there's no way I'm parting with my Chloe. The same goes for all the rest. They're my life, Mr Taylor, my life,' she said. 'I'll make sure they don't mix with any other cats.'

Three months later the test results were just the same. The positives were still positive but none of the indoors cats had become infected. Mrs Woodford's isolation ward was working.

Chloe was still sneezing but not so badly as before and her gums were looking less inflamed.

'Chloe's antibiotics seem to be helping a bit,' I said hopefully, 'and the other three aren't showing any signs of ill health at all. That's good. Time will tell if the infection's going to make them really ill.' Chloe didn't seem bothered a bit by all the fuss.

'I'm not taking in any more strays, just for the moment,' Mrs Woodford told me as we stood in the kitchen watching the 'indoors' cats at play. 'It wouldn't be fair. I'm ever so grateful to your friend but he can't go on testing my cats for nothing for ever.'

I smiled. 'I'm sure he wouldn't mind. His boss might, but Ian's a great cat lover. His company's working on a vaccine against feline leukaemia right now. They're using all the latest genetic engineering techniques. It'll be a big breakthrough. It might even lead to a vaccine against AIDS itself.'

Mrs Woodford smiled approvingly. 'All this talk of wonderful breakthroughs and new vaccines is lovely of course and I wish it could have helped my poor Tommy and Sam. But sometimes when we go on about all this marvellous progress we forget about the animals and what they really need most of all.'

'What's that, Mrs Woodford?' I asked, intrigued.

She paused for a moment, then reached down to the cats at her feet and picked up Tigger, the oldest in the house, and gave him a huge hug as he purred and purred.

32

'I've never seen Katy looking so smart.'

The golden cocker spaniel stood disconsolately on my consulting room table. She was so well groomed I thought she'd be off to Cruft's any minute.

'I know,' said Dave Pritchard. 'I thought if I treated her to a wash and brush up at the dog clipper's it would cheer her up. She's been miserable for days. My wife tells me a perm works wonders when you're feeling down in the dumps. So I thought if it works for her, it'll work for Katy.'

She didn't look too happy to me.

'She's been like this for a good few days now. She took a nasty tumble out on the river the other day. You know how she likes to jump in and out of my boat. Well, she took a run at one of the dinghies moored next to it and missed her footing. Down she went with a crash.'

I liked Katy. I used to see her a lot when I went out sailing with friends on the River Yealm. Devon's full of lovely places but Newton Ferrers has got to be one of the loveliest. It's only a small village and the houses nestle into the hillside as they stretch out along the river. In the summer the whole place comes to life. There are boats everywhere. Tiny dinghies, racing yachts, even the odd floating gin palace. Dave Pritchard's always on the river and wherever he goes Katy goes too.

'What you might call a natural seadog,' he told me one day as I watched her bustling round the busy moorings. 'But just to be on the safe side I always make her wear that lifejacket. Bought it special, I did. It's great for the kids who come here, you know. If Katy's got her lifejacket on they don't mind wearing theirs. Proper job.'

But today I don't think Katy could have cared less whether she ever went to sea again. She was dead miserable.

'Could be a fall, Dave. That would make her sore,' I said as the small dog winced in pain as I palpated her abdomen. 'She seems really tender. Could be bruising.'

I'm often told a vet's job is difficult. After all they say your patients can't speak. How on earth do you know what's wrong with them? The answer's always there if you look hard enough, examine them properly and sometimes ignore totally what the owner's telling you.

Katy was very ill all right, but it was nothing to do with any fall. She'd got tired of standing there as Dave and I talked. With a resigned sigh she suddenly sat down and I thought she was going to collapse. And there it was, the clue I needed. Pus. Not a lot, but just a trace. Enough to point me in the right direction.

'It's not her back at all, Dave, it's her womb. It's

212

infected,' I told him. 'I should have guessed. She's got a pyometra. No wonder she's miserable.' When bitches develop womb infections it makes them really ill. You usually see them a few weeks after they've had a season. Sometimes the owner has no trouble noticing a smelly discharge from down below, but if the bitch's cervix stays closed then there's little sign of that and the owner hasn't got a clue. These hidden pyometras can kill.

'She had an injection last time she came into season. We'd sailed up to Cowes and Katy just got carried away. You know what Cowes Week is like,' Dave smiled. 'Anyway, we didn't want her to have pups so we popped her along to a vet to stop her getting pregnant.'

'A misalliance. Of course. Sometimes that's all the hormonal stimulus it takes to start one of these infections off. I bet she's been feeling grim for ages,' I continued. 'There's only one thing to do. We'll have to operate. Now.'

You'd think antibiotics would be the thing to clear up any old infection, wouldn't you? But often they're no use at all. They don't seem to be able to mop up all the infection you find with most pyometras. If you put off surgery there's a good chance you'll put the bitch's life at risk.

'I don't want Suzy operated on, Mr Taylor. She's too old,' Mrs Nurse had told me when I'd explained that her nine-year-old dachshund had pyometra. 'Just put her on antibiotics, please.'

You can't argue with a client if their mind's made up. I put Suzy on antibiotics and they helped a bit but the next time she came into season we were back to square one.

'She needs surgery, Mrs Nurse,' I explained gently. 'She's much sicker than she looks. If you like I can do a blood test. Her white cell count will soon confirm my diagnosis.'

'If she's that sick, she won't stand the surgery,' Mrs Nurse replied tartly. 'And I don't want to lose her.'

I didn't either. But it was no use. For three days I cajoled her, pleaded with her and almost bullied her into letting me help her dog. I was getting desperate. Suzy was becoming sicker all the time.

At nine o'clock Mrs Nurse came to the surgery.

'I'm still not sure this operation's a good idea,' she said. 'There's still a chance she'll pull through without it.' At eleven she was back again. Suzy was dead in her arms. I could have punched the wall. Six months ago I'd told her what needed to be done and now the poor dog was dead. The toxins inside her had become too much for her body to cope with. Her kidneys had failed and she had died. What a waste. I could have saved her if only I'd been given the chance.

Dave Pritchard didn't hesitate when I told him I wanted to operate on Katy straight away.

'Whatever she needs, Nigel,' he said. 'I just want her well again.'

You've got to be very careful when you anaesthetise a bitch with a pyometra. Sometimes they're so ill and dehydrated that the first thing they need is an intravenous drip to have even a chance of getting through the operation.

Katy sat uncomplainingly on the operating table as I clipped her leg and inserted the indwelling catheter into her vein. I could use that to give her the anaesthetic and give her any fluids she needed. As the anaesthetic took hold she yawned, and Louise, my nurse, gently held her jaws apart while I slid the endotracheal tube into position. She'd need that to breathe through during the operation. Soon she was fast asleep as with each breath she took in more and more halothane.

I scrubbed up while Louise prepared Katy's abdomen for surgery. If you make a quick bold incision down the midline there's hardly any blood.

When the summer solstice comes I can guarantee I'll always see my two favourite hippies, Genghis and Attila. Two of the softest German Shepherd crosses you'll ever meet from here to Stonehenge.

'It's their mum, mister. She's ill like. These two, well they're nearly two months old now. She's not been too good ever since she had 'em.' There were three of them. Two guys and a girl. Travellers on their way from Cornwall to Glastonbury for a festival, they said. 'We ain't got much money like. The RSPCA said to come and see you. You'd help.'

'I'll do what I can,' I replied. 'She's in a bad way, though. She's got a really bad womb infection. She'll need surgery straight away.'

'Anything you say, man,' they said together. 'We've been trying some natural herbal remedies but it's you she needs now.'

We carried Sarah to the operating theatre and they helped me as I started to operate. The girl cuddled Attila and Genghis as I tried to save their mother. Gentle, laid-back puppies. Just like the travellers who owned them.

We finished Sarah's operation and I laid her carefully onto some heated bedding in the corner of the room. The four of us sat around and talked as the night grew later and Sarah grew weaker. They told me of their life on the road. I'm not sure I fancied it much. There didn't seem to be much chance of getting a bath too often if these three and the dogs were anything to go by. But you couldn't help liking them. They spent most winters in Ireland and in the summer drove their home, an old retired ambulance, all over the West Country. I've never met three people more contented.

As we talked the German Shepherd slipped softly away from us. She was in no more pain or discomfort and like so many of my chums over the years the last thing she ever knew was kind words and tenderness. The two puppies nuzzled her gently and once she'd finally gone they sat curled up beside her.

Suddenly there was a loud commotion outside the surgery window. Lots of shouting and foul language and then the sound of smashing glass.

Vandals. Coming home from the pub, nothing better to do than smash things up. Just another Friday night. A couple of smashed windows and there all over the road the bits of plastic that were the remains of my brand new surgery sign. Mindless destruction. Even a young beech sapling we'd planted only the week before had been snapped in two.

The travellers and I rushed outside and when I saw the damage I could have cried. 'How could anyone do this?' I moaned. 'There we are, trying to do some good. Don't they understand?'

'Some people never will,' one of the travellers said as they helped me clear away the mess. 'They're not at peace with themselves, that's all. They see the world as something you've got to destroy. They don't know it, but that's their loss, really. We've got a long way to go before we're as happy with our lives as half those animals you look after.'

I still see Genghis and Attila when the days grow longer and midsummer's just round the corner. They're fine dogs, relaxed and friendly. At peace with themselves and the world. I'm always pleased when the rusty old ambulance pulls into my car park and they leap out to see me. Old friends. My hippies are back in town.

Katy's womb was enormous. Huge and distended with infection. I thought it might burst before I could remove it. I worked as quickly and delicately as I could. Clamping off blood vessels as I went, I worked it free of her body. She'd start to feel much better now with that thing gone.

'I've never seen her looking so well,' Dave Pritchard

told me one afternoon a month or two later as we stood and watched her at play with the young boys and girls from the sailing school. 'In fact she's so active now I can't keep up with her. I wish I'd realised she was ill but I didn't have a clue until you spotted what was wrong with her.'

I knew what he meant. There's a lot to be said for looking at things with another pair of eyes.

33

'It's Gregory Peck. I've squashed him.'

If Robert Winston-Frost was giving a lecture, you just had to be there. Pure theatre. You knew in your heart that, given half the chance, he wouldn't be a veterinary surgeon at all. He wasn't really cut out for things clinical. A song and dance man. The cheeky chappie with a smile and a joke for everyone.

He could have been the Billy Graham of veterinary medicine if he'd had the breaks. A real enthusiast. He could work an audience like an old-time evangelist and have them eating out of the palm of his hand in minutes. We loved it. Today he pranced around the stage at the front of the lecture theatre with a little white cardboard box in his right hand. He asked us what we might think would be inside and we roared our suggestions.

'A mouse.'

'Your false teeth.'

'Barry Snowdon's packed lunch.'

The place was in uproar.

'No, never. Never, ladies and gentlemen. Nowhere near it.'

A loud cry of 'Shame, shame' filled the room.

'Ladies and gentlemen, boys and girls I have in this little box here the veterinary surgeon's favourite friend. THE BUGGERYJAR.'

That was it. We were gone. Helpless with laughter.

'Today ladies and gentlemen,' he paused, 'boys and girls, I am going to tell you all you need to know about the BUGGERYJAR. By the time I've finished you will know how to tell when a BUGGERYJAR is sick and when it is healthy. You will be BUGGERYJAR experts.'

He opened the lid of the cardboard box and with a flourish pulled out a plastic budgie.

'Not much you can do for this one,' he said with a wicked grin and tossed it into the crowded rows of students. 'Anyone good at the kiss of life?'

A small, dapper man, always immaculately dressed, you'd see him strolling the corridors of the Beaumont Animal Hospital in a spotless white coat or more often his favourite blazer and grey flannel trousers. You got the impression he spent hours preening himself before a mirror in his office until he felt smart enough to venture out amongst the patients and their owners.

He could do a great Buggeryjar impersonation.

'This is a happy budgie.'

He expanded his chest, put his short arms rigidly behind him and cocked his head to one side.

'Who's a pretty boy, then,' we all cried. He was delighted.

'This poor buggeryjar is pretty sick.' He dropped his head, let his arms hang disconsolately at his side

220

and bobbed up and down a bit on one leg. 'He'll never play the piano again.'

'Ahh,' we roared. 'Shame, shame.'

It was better than the panto.

For an hour he took us through the budgie book of health. He covered everything from scaly beak to being egg bound. A difficult one, that.

A tip here, a joke there, and time and time again he captured a clinical disorder with a nod of his head or a shake of his body. And the marvellous thing was you remembered all he said and what he was trying to teach you. A bravura performance of observation. The key to understanding all animal disease.

'I didn't know how to get him here. So I put him in this.' Stella Johnstone laid a small white cardboard box on the consulting table. 'It's my fault, really. I tripped over and fell on him. Poor bird.'

Of course, Gregory Peck was a buggeryjar. I should have guessed.

'He was on the floor playing with a cotton reel. He often does that. I went to answer the phone and I tripped over him. Fell right on top of him I did, and now he's squeaking like this.'

Gregory was never going to play the handsome male lead again. He was lucky to be alive. I could be wrong, but Mrs Johnstone looked as though she might weigh about twelve stone. Poor old Greg must have thought the end of the world had come. One instant eclipse and that was it. No more cotton reels.

'There's nothing broken, Mrs Johnstone,' I said

encouragingly, 'but I think he's always going to squeak like this. You would too if you'd been squashed like he had.'

'I didn't know what to do, Mr Taylor,' she said. 'I mean, how do you give a budgie first aid?'

As Gregory Peck waddled across my consulting table I could tell he was getting better by the minute. Mrs Johnstone was relieved. 'I'm glad I didn't kill him. I don't know how I ever would have got over that,' she said as she left clutching the cardboard box. 'I don't care if he always squeaks like this.'

Some people get carried away when their animals are ill. If they've got a little bit of first aid knowledge it can sometimes be a dangerous thing. Bloody dangerous.

Pat Collins came rushing to my door in Helston.

'It's my budgie, mate. I've blown it up.'

He was a winchman with the search and rescue helicopters at Culdrose. He wouldn't tell you but I knew how brave he was. Dangling from the thinnest of wires he'd plucked eight men from the sea during the Fastnet race that had ended in disaster the year before. They owed their lives to him and all the other aircrew who'd put out to save them in some of the worst weather I could ever remember in Cornwall. He'd been trained as a paramedic and had to resuscitate two of the men on the helicopter as they flew back to Treliske hospital in Truro.

'When the budgie collapsed I thought, aye aye, that's it, he's had a heart attack,' he explained to me hurriedly. 'He just lay there dead like, so I thought I got to get his heart going again. Quick.'

On the helicopters Pat had the proper paddles that could send a surge of high voltage electricity through your heart and get it beating once more.

'So I thinks to myself, how the hell am I going to get his heart beating? The wife's there blowing her hair dry. That's it, I'll grab that, pull the dryer off it and put the electric wires across its chest.'

I knew what was coming next.

'I forgot the domestic supply's AC not DC. Once I switched the plug on the current just kept surging through him till the whole lot shorted. The bugger exploded and caught fire.'

'Bloody hell,' I said. 'First aid with a vengeance.'

There was nothing I could do. The tiny bird was long past my help.

Mrs Collins wasn't too amused. Her budgie was done to a frazzle and her hair still wasn't dry. 'I told him it was no good. The bird wasn't even breathing, Mr Taylor. Dead as they come it was. Always the bloody hero, that's Pat's trouble. Still, at least it didn't suffer.'

Pat Collins was lucky to be alive. He could have killed himself.

Boy George was only about a year old. A green budgie, he lived in the Waltons' bedroom. He'd been fine till they decided to fix a mirror to the ceiling. I'd have put one next to the wardrobe, but there you are, interior design was never one of my strong points.

'He keeps being sick,' Mrs Walton told me. 'It's a right pain, I can tell you.'

'It's the mirror, Mrs Walton,' I said as we stood in the middle of the bedroom discussing Boy George. On cue he brought up lunch. 'He can see himself in it and like a lot of male birds he fancies himself silly.' For lots of male budgies it's a normal part of courtship behaviour.

'You mean there's nothing wrong with him?' she said with a smile.

'No,' I blushed. 'He's just oversexed, that's all. Nothing a cold shower wouldn't put right. If you move him out of the bedroom he'll be fine.'

If only they could talk. James Herriot had a point.

When Peterkins the budgie died on Christmas Eve it broke Cyril Price's heart.

'I don't think I'll ever get over it, Mr Taylor. I wish I'd brought him to you. Trichomoniasis he had. Trichomoniasis. He could have got better, you know. If only the other vet had known how to treat him.'

Cyril sobbed as he told me. He had another budgie Prudence and he was sure she had the same thing. 'She keeps on being sick and I know it's because she's ill.'

I reached for the budgie textbook I always keep handy in the surgery. For tiny creatures they've had an awful lot written about them.

'Don't worry, Mr Price,' I told him. 'It says here we should be able to get her better with a single dose of metronidazole, an antibiotic. Let's give it a try.'

'Oh, thank you, Mr Taylor. I've been reading loads of budgie books trying to find out why Peterkins died. That's what they all suggest for treatment. I wish the other vet had tried it. Do you know, he told me not to worry because Peterkins was only a budgie.'

He paused and composed himself.

I comforted him as best I could and got on with treating Prudence. She wasn't too keen on the taste of her medicine. The textbook said a single dose would be enough. It was.

'Wonderful, Mr Taylor. Wonderful. She's never looked back. I've brought you a present,' he said excitedly when next he came to the surgery. 'It'll be very helpful for you.'

It was a brown paper parcel tied up with some ragged old string. Inside were a hundred or so pages of beautifully typed information about budgie diseases. There were wonderful diagrams and flow charts showing you how to diagnose anything your budgie might fall ill with. It was a labour of love. If I'd been writing a thesis for a PhD I couldn't have done better.

'It's marvellous,' I said. 'It'll be really useful.'

'I know,' he said. 'I spent ages going through all the books I could find and putting all this information together. It's the least I could do for Peterkins.'

To Cyril Price Peterkins was a small feathered person. I know exactly what he means. Whenever I see a budgie in the surgery I don't see a bird at all. I see Robert Winston-Frost. He is dancing up and down on one leg. And he is making me laugh.

34

I'd never hijacked a Mother's Pride bread van before.

These are the days of miracle and wonder. If you don't believe me, take a trip across Goonhilly Downs, not far from Helston. There, rising out of the mist most mornings, you'll see where the space age meets rural Cornwall. Giant satellite dishes that beam communications all around the globe and, for all I know, out across the ether right into ET's back yard.

I often used to see the satellite dishes, groaning and creaking as they turned skywards to receive their invisible signals, as I rattled about over the Cornish countryside in my beat up old Morris Traveller. Woodworm on wheels. Being a country vet is a bit like blasting off into orbit every day. You launch yourself from the surgery each morning and hurtle around narrow country lanes like a meteor with a death wish and aim for splashdown late in the evening, hopefully not too far from the nearest pub.

I was rushing that day to get to George Trevan's farm near Traboe. Trouble at Traboe was all I needed.

It was the Ministry of Agriculture who had warned us, about a week before. Foot and mouth in Brittany.

Someone had come up with the comforting suspicion that birds could bring it over to the West Country. No joke; foot and mouth is bad news however it arrives.

The last time we had a major outbreak back in the mid-sixties it caused havoc. In the United Kingdom we've never used vaccines to control it, or treated any unfortunate cattle that have caught it. That's never been considered an economic option. If a cow or bull is found on a farm with foot and mouth, all the cattle living there are slaughtered. Thousands of cows were slaughtered and at one time, because the outbreaks were being reported thick and fast, there was a serious danger the Ministry would run out of vets to deal with it. The whole of the final year at the Royal Veterinary College were sworn in as temporary ministry inspectors the day they passed their final exams. Then off they went, newly qualified, in a couple of coaches to Shropshire, the worst affected county. It was a pretty grim start.

They drum it into you at veterinary school. Look for blisters in the mouth and on the tongue. The cow drools a lot. The cow goes lame. Look for blisters on its feet, in between the claws. It'll have a high temperature. You get the impression that if you ever missed a case they'd take you round the back of the barn and shoot you. It's every vet's nightmare: the foot and mouth you failed to diagnose.

'I've got a young bull who's gone lame. Can you come take a look at him?' George Trevan had asked when he rang the practice. The other vets were already out on their rounds. I was seeing a couple of dogs and a ferret. Well, ferrets get sick too, you know; as a matter of fact a ferret with the runs is a none too pleasant diagnostic challenge. 'And by the way, I'm a little bit worried because he seems to be drooling a little bit too. Slobbering like hell he is, actually. You'd better come quick.' Just my luck. The call no one ever wants.

I hurried off to Traboe as fast as the beat up Morris Traveller would take me. No, George must be mistaken. It couldn't be as bad as I thought.

It was.

'I don't like the look of this, George,' I said as I examined the young Friesian bull in one of the loose boxes. 'Look there. You can see why he's lame. See those vesicles in between his claws? I bet they're sore.'

I took his temperature. It was rocketing.

'And I'm not too keen on all this salivating. I can't see any blisters on his tongue but you never know, they might be on their way. I've had a good look in his mouth, there's nothing stuck there.' I once had a Highland cow swallow a Coke can which got lodged at the back of its tongue. If only I could find a foreign body now, my worries would be over.

George has been breeding fine pedigree Friesians for over thirty years. He could tell I was worried.

'You don't think the pigs have given him something, do you?' he said anxiously. 'They've been in the pen next to him for about a week now. We bought 'em in. No telling what they was carrying, see.'

God. Pigs. They can carry foot and mouth. There'd

been a lot of swine vesicular disease about too, which looks just like it. Even if they had blisters it would take laboratory tests to confirm any diagnosis. Thirty pigs. They'd all have to be checked. Things were going from bad to worse.

'Had a guy here yesterday from the Friesian Society. He was looking at all my bulls. He had a real good look at this one. Said if he didn't get better to call the vet. There were no blisters or anything then. He was just lame, that's all. The guy's in Holland today.'

'What?' I asked incredulously.

'He's in Holland, visiting some of their top Friesian breeders. He's assessing the bulls for the Society.'

I swallowed hard.

'George, we've got to do something quick. I'm not sure, but this bull could have foot and mouth. If any vet is at all suspicious he's got to report it.'

I left him looking stunned in the yard and ran as fast as I could for the house. I needed the phone.

'Hello, John, it's Nigel. Can you ring the Ministry in Redruth for me. It's urgent.' My boss had returned from his morning rounds. I explained my worries.

'Right,' he said. 'Stay where you are. I'll get the Ministry vets out there straight away. If anyone comes to the farm, don't let them leave. If it is foot and mouth it can be spread just like that. Remember, no one leaves the farm till the Ministry get there.'

George and his wife sat in the farmhouse kitchen. I'd been there loads of time. After calvings late at night they'd make you supper or at lunchtime, during blood testing, they'd serve you a slap-up meal. Cornish farmhouse kitchens are lovely places. Warm and happy.

But not today. You could have cut the gloom with a knife.

'The whole lot, Mr Taylor? Not the whole lot, surely? They all have to die? I hope you're wrong.' Mrs Trevan was close to tears as I told her all that you had to do to deal with foot and mouth.

'I hope so too, but only the Ministry can confirm if an animal has foot and mouth. I have to tell them if I'm suspicious. If any vet missed it the consequences are just too terrible to think of.'

It seemed to take ages for the Ministry vets to arrive. As we waited I hoped we wouldn't get any visitors.

I was out of luck.

'Morning, Mrs Trevan. There was no one about like in the yard so I come straight on in. Do you need any groceries today?' It was Mike Bolitho. A lot of the farmers' wives bought a few odds and ends from Mike's mobile shop. He called in at least twice a week. He'd be calling at every farm for miles if I didn't stop him quick.

'I'm sorry,' I said authoritatively, 'there's a suspected disease outbreak on this farm. You'll have to stay till the Ministry of Agriculture get here.'

'Foot and mouth, Mike,' George said sombrely. 'Foot and mouth. The vet here thinks I've got a bull with foot and mouth. You've got to stay put.'

'Christ,' exclaimed Mike. 'That's the last thing

anyone round here needs. Put on the kettle Mrs T., I'm going nowhere.'

I said, 'George, we'll have to send someone up to the farm gate to stop people coming in. It's about a mile, isn't it, up to the main road? Perhaps your son Bobby can run up there before anyone else arrives and tell any visitors to push off.'

The tanker driver from the dairy hurtled into the yard from nowhere. I'm sure the main qualification you need for driving round the farms picking up milk from bulk tanks is a personal recommendation from Alain Prost. I often met these guys and their twenty-ton tankers as I hurried on my rounds. They were always in a hurry. This one was no exception.

'Bloody hell,' he said when I told him he'd be staying put. 'I haven't got all day to waste sitting round here. I'll ring the depot and see what they say.'

'You can ring them,' I said slowly and deliberately, 'but whatever they say, you're staying. You might as well sit down and have a cup of tea with Mike Bolitho here. I'm sure the Ministry vets won't be long.'

As Bobby raced for the farm entrance a white Mercedes sped along the muddy track. He tried to wave it down but the driver took no notice and pulled into the yard at speed.

Graham Nancekeville. A farmer I didn't like one little bit. 'You be careful with my cow, mind. She's a valuable heifer. I don't want her mucked about by some newly qualified amateur. Watch what you're doing.'

Some farmers really like young vets.

231

I'd been called out to cleanse one of Graham Nancekeville's cows. She'd just had a calf but the afterbirth hadn't come away. Anywhere else in the country, once she'd had a calf she wouldn't be a heifer at all, but in Devon and Cornwall cows can be nearly thirty and drawing their pensions and they're still heifers.

'I'll be careful,' I said unenthusiastically. 'I've done a few cleansings before, you know.'

But never one like this. As I placed my lubricated, gloved hand into her, I was amazed. It was as if all her internal anatomy had vanished. There was just one big hole where everything should be. She was torn terribly.

'What the hell's been going on?' I said angrily. 'Who on earth calved this cow?'

'I did,' he said at once. 'No more difficult than usual. I don't know what your problem is. I thought you were a bit of an expert.' With that he turned and left the loosebox. 'I've got better things to do than hang round here watching a novice at work. Joe will help you.'

Joe, one of the farmhands, climbed over the gate and stood beside the cow. He said nothing till Nancekeville was out of sight. But I could tell he was furious.

'Do you know what that bastard did?' he asked me angrily. 'Only pulled her poor bloody calf off her with a tractor. Me and Fred, we'd been trying for ages to pull her off with ropes. Nancekeville said we were wasting our time. Tied the calving ropes to the tractor and tugged it out of her. Tore her to hell, I expect. You should have heard her bellow. The poor bloody calf was dead too. What a cock up.'

That was it. No wonder he didn't want me to poke about inside. Didn't want me to find the truth.

'She'll have to be slaughtered, too, Joe. She can't live like this. Infection will set in and it'll be a hell of a painful death. The bugger. I could swing for him.'

The circumstances of this latest meeting were just as unpromising. Graham Nancekeville got out of his Mercedes.

'I'm here to see Mr Trevan. I'm thinking of buying a couple of his Friesian bulls. He's expecting me.'

In all the worry of the morning George had clean forgotten.

'I'm sorry Graham. Mr Taylor says you'll have to stay. One of my bulls is ill. It might be foot and mouth.'

'Nonsense, that young twerp doesn't know what he's talking about. He's already cost me one of my best heifers and now he's trying to worry you unnecessarily. He's an idiot.'

'I don't think so,' said George Trevan determinedly. 'There's been a lot of warnings about this on Radio Cornwall and the TV. They've got a lot of it in France, you know. I hope to God he's not right, but he could be.'

'George, that's a chance you'll have to take. I'm not staying here any longer if this fool's in charge.' He headed back towards his car.

'You're staying,' I shouted loudly.

'You make me,' he replied angrily, and squared up towards me.

Mike Bolitho and the tanker driver stood on the steps of the farmhouse. They'd heard raised voices and had come out to see what the fuss was about.

'Looks like a punch-up to me,' I heard Mike say.

'Any second now,' the tanker driver chirped.

You know how there's always a moment in the westerns when the wagon train's being attacked by the Indians and you don't think anyone's got a chance of avoiding being scalped, and just then the cavalry arrives? As Graham Nancekeville and I eyed each other menacingly the cavalry arrived for me too. Only it wasn't General Custer. It was the man from Mother's Pride.

Bobby Trevan had waved furiously at him to stop as he met him halfway up the farm track. The man from Mother's Pride obviously didn't twig what Bobby was getting at. The man from Mother's Pride waved back and drove on blissfully unaware of any problem. He had doughnuts to deliver.

As the van drove into the yard I took my chance. If I didn't do something quickly Nancekeville would be driving out of the farm and spreading havoc everywhere. Before anyone could move I ran over to the van, pulled the sliding door back and jumped aboard.

'What the hell are you doing?' the driver yelled.

'No time for questions. Just turn this bloody van round and drive like hell for that gate. We've got to block it off before the Mercedes there can leave the yard.'

'Right mate, whatever you say. You seem pretty desperate.'

He spun the van round in a circle and slithered to a halt across the farmyard gate as a sea of saffron buns and nelson squares threatened to submerge us. There was no way any vehicle was getting in or out of George Trevan's yard.

Graham Nancekeville was not impressed. He stood there demanding the van be removed. The man from Mother's Pride stood his ground.

Mike Bolitho and the tanker driver had had enough of Graham's temper. 'Here, come and have a lovely cup of tea with us,' they said as they gently ushered him, one each side of him, into the farmhouse. 'Mrs Trevan makes a lovely cup of tea. You'd love one, now wouldn't you?'

It's not easy to refuse when one arm's tightly held behind your back.

'You get on with your job, mate. We'll take care of this gentleman,' the tanker driver shouted over.

As George and I explained to the puzzled Mother's Pride delivery man just what was going on, the Ministry vets arrived. At last. They clambered past the bread van.

They looked like two lost lifeboatmen as they strode around the farmyard in their regulation issue black macs, protective overtrousers, wellington boots and sou'westers.

'Can't take any chances,' the senior man said. 'Where's the bull?'

235

We went over to the loose box and they examined the young Friesian.

'He's got a high temperature all right. Lots of salivation but I can't see any vesicles in his mouth. We'll have to cast him to check his feet.'

I quickly ran a rope around the bull. If you tie a knot round his neck and pass the rope back towards the tail, looping it round his body as you go, you can pull him to the floor. It only takes a gentle tug. At least that's what they tell you in all the animal husbandry books I've ever read. It took nearly twenty minutes for George, me and the Ministry vets to pull him to the ground. He didn't want to play. He obviously hadn't read the same books.

'We'll take some samples from these vesicles between his claws and send them off to Weybridge. The Ministry laboratory can soon confirm if it's foot and mouth,' the younger vet said. 'We'll have to check the pigs too.'

It took ages for them to finish their checks. They're paid to be thorough. Eventually, about two hours after they'd arrived, they huddled in a corner of the farmyard discussing their findings.

'What do you think?' I asked, 'Is it foot and mouth?'

They thought for a moment and then the older man replied.

'It's only the Minister of Agriculture himself who can confirm a case of foot and mouth and that's after all the necessary tests have been carried out. There's no vesicles in the bull's mouth but otherwise it could well have been the real thing.'

'So are we in the clear?' I asked anxiously.

'I think so. The pigs show no sign of illness and it's more likely the bull has got a less serious infection. I've got an idea the lymph nodes in the back of his throat are starting to swell. They'll do that if they're mopping up infection. That would explain the salivation. We should be able to tell you what's happening for sure once we've had our samples tested.' George was relieved. If the Ministry vets were right he could breathe again.

As it turned out they were right. The bull had an infection, but it was caused by a bacteria, Fusiformis necrophorus, not a virus. It's the sort of thing that comes on very suddenly and can make a cow or bull very ill and uncomfortable, especially if it has a high temperature. They don't always salivate, but George Trevan's bull did. The body's lymph system is there to deal with threatening infections. If you cut your thumb you'll often feel a lump like an egg come up, usually high in your armpit or your throat. That's the lymph nodes at work. If you've ever had really bad tonsillitis you'll know exactly how George Trevan's bull felt.

'You're all free to go,' the senior Ministry vet said. 'It was pretty close, though.'

If the Ministry vets had been convinced it was foot and mouth we'd have all had to stay there while they disinfected our vehicles and brought us changes of clothing. Like everyone else I was itching to get away. The practice calls had probably been piling up all morning. In Holland the man from the Friesian

Society had been traced to one of the farms he'd been due to visit and told to stay put. Now he could go free again too and there were several Dutch farmers who ended the morning more relieved than when they started it.

The Ministry vets gave Graham Nancekeville a lecture about his responsibility to other farmers and I had the distinct impression Mike Bolitho and the tanker driver had given him a lesson in manners he probably wouldn't forget. If I'd told them about the heifer he'd damaged so badly I'm sure they would have chinned him.

'Slice of luck I came along, wasn't it,' the man from Mother's Pride said as he climbed back into his van. 'You see much of this foot and mouth, then? I can see why you was so worried. I've never been hijacked before. Quite exciting, really.'

'Some excitement you can do without,' I said. 'I can honestly say I've never ever seen a case of foot and mouth. And I'll tell you something else.'

'What's that?' he said expectantly.

'I hope to hell I never do.'

35

There was only one place to be that afternoon. Wally's bar. It wasn't much of a bar really. Just somewhere you could pick up a pie and a pint. And today, somewhere you could sit and wait for your exam results.

Finals. Never. Nearly five years flashed away just like that. And now you had two weeks to show them you could make it. Two weeks before they let you loose, a veterinary surgeon at last.

I was beginning to think I was never going to do anything but sit exams. Five years of end-of-term exams, mid-term exams and professional exams. Now I had to cram all that information in my head and go for it. God, I never wanted to study again.

'Perhaps you would be kind enough to tell us exactly what you see on that X-ray, Mr Taylor,' Donald Neville, the professor of small animal surgery from Liverpool Veterinary School, asked me. Part of the fun of finals was that they asked vets from the other veterinary schools to come and examine you.

'It's a cat,' I replied cautiously. 'I think it's swallowed a foreign body.'

There was what looked like a large sewing needle

lodged right in the middle of its abdomen. But they don't give you easy X-rays like that. There must be something else.

'What else can you see?' Professor Neville continued. I'd heard about Professor Neville's X-rays before. They often looked simple just to lead you into a trap.

His favourite was the 'pregnant' bitch. It had been doing the rounds for years. You tell him it's pregnant. He congratulates you on your observation and then asks you how many pups she's going to have. Five, you say. That's how many skeletons you can see. Then he tells you to look again. Failed. She might have one live puppy if she's lucky. She's already eaten the rest. They're in her stomach, not her womb. It's all there plain to see when he tells you. If only you'd read the X-ray properly.

'I'm not happy with her abdomen, sir,' I say at last. 'I can see the needle, but there's very little sign of much else where her intestines should be.'

'Where are her intestines, then, Mr Taylor? Can you see them?' Suddenly the penny drops. She's swallowed a needle all right but that was probably yonks ago. It hasn't bothered her at all. Not like the car accident she had later.

'They're displaced, sir,' I reply. 'I think I can see them in her chest. There's a good chance she has a ruptured diaphragm. One or two of her ribs are broken.'

'Very good. Now we're getting somewhere. How could you confirm your diagnosis?'

'Well sir. I'm happy with what I see but I suppose if you wanted you could give her some contrast.'

'What would that do?'

'Make her intestines show up white. Then I'd know for sure where they were. I'd see them easily if they'd slipped through a diaphragmatic tear into her chest.'

'Very good. Do most clinicians do that?'

'If I was in practice I probably wouldn't.'

'Why not?'

'She's already having enough difficulty breathing and I could make things a whole lot worse trying to make her swallow contrast medium she doesn't want.'

Robert Winston-Frost smiled. Examiners always work in twos. The hard man and the soft man.

'Thank you Mr Taylor. I think it's always important that we consider our patients' comfort, don't you?'

I started to relax; perhaps I was getting somewhere.

'Perhaps you'd like to tell me how you would surgically repair that poor cat's ruptured diaphragm.'

And on it went. Days of hanging around draughty barns half nervous. Avoiding all your pals just in case they told you horror stories of how they'd got on and all the mistakes they'd made. Or worse still wound you up with tales of how easy it all was. The first week of written exams then five days of non-stop clinical quizzing had been bad enough. This second week of practicals seemed endless.

'Which leg is she lame on, Mr Taylor?' Barry Snowdon asked me as a chestnut mare was led backwards and forwards in front of me at the trot.

This always got me. It can still catch me out even

today. Pick the wrong leg and you look a real dough-nut. Get it right and the horse owners think you can walk on water.

The trick is to watch and see which leg she isn't keen to put weight on. If a horse is trotting on concrete or any hard surface you'll also pick up anything that's wrong by the sound the hooves make as the horse clatters by. Clip, clip, clip, bonk is pretty diagnostic. Another good dodge which I caught onto years later is that when an owner rings and tells you her horse is lame you ask her to bandage it. I like yellow but the colour's up to you. It doesn't do a bit of good but it doesn't half look impressive when you go straight to the lame leg. They fall for it every time.

'Well, Mr Taylor. Which leg do you want to have a look at?'

This was it. No chance of getting out of it. Not a stable bandage in sight.

'I'll go for both the forelegs, Mr Snowdon,' I said confidently, like the expert I wished I was. 'She looks uncomfortable on both of them to me.'

John, the college groom, gave me an encouraging wink. I could be on the right track.

'Thank you. Now can you tell me how you'd make a proper diagnosis of her problem.'

I explained how I'd inject local anaesthetic into the nerves of her front legs to deaden them. If you blocked the right nerve she'd go sound. You'd then know which bones to X-ray. I was sounding confident.

Quite suddenly there in the fine spring sunshine I realised how far I'd come since that first day at

Camden Town. Then I didn't have much of a clue about any animal's anatomy, even mine, never mind the horse. And here I was outlining to Barry Snowdon, *Barry Snowdon*, every little anatomical feature of a horse's foot I'd become familiar with.

Frank Merlen would have been delighted. He taught us equine anatomy in the second year and he led me through my anatomy exams that year as if he was leading a lost soul.

'That long muscle, Mr Taylor, extending over the digits,' he'd say, pointing at the specimen leg hanging before us, 'what would you say it was called?'

'The long digital extensor, Mr Merlen.'

'Marvellous, marvellous. Couldn't be anything else.' He'd point to another muscle. 'And this one here. Just cranial to the tibia?'

'The cranial tibial,' I'd say. This was easy.

'Marvellous, marvellous. Couldn't be anything else.'

Confidence. That's what he gave me. I'm still grateful to him today.

And if there's one thing you really need in the middle of finals, it's confidence. Barry Snowdon led me to an X-ray viewer on which three or four films were being displayed. 'So you've done all that. The nerve blocks have worked and you've taken these X-rays.'

'It's navicular disease,' I said. 'You can see the signs of it all over these navicular bones. She's got it bad.'

Barry Snowdon grinned. I was there. I could have kissed him.

One more exam to go. Meat inspection and public health. Most of my year had already finished and were drinking Wally out of beer faster than he could fetch the barrels from the cellar. I didn't dare go near the place.

Already rumours were flying as to who had passed and who hadn't. Betty Bright, one of the girls in our year, was convinced she had.

'They told me they'll see me in the Beaumont, Monday morning,' she chirped relentlessly. 'I've applied to be houseman there, so I'm sure I'm through.' I kept well away. Optimism was the last thing I needed with one more oral exam to go.

Half an hour on meat inspection. I didn't want to know about that. Not many of us did, back then. Today it's different. Mad cow disease and salmonella have seen to that. Veterinary public health has become more important than ever. But all I ever wanted to do was look after dogs and cats. So I might go and work in a farm or equine practice for some years, but meat inspection? No, my heart wasn't in meat inspection. The examiners soon cottoned on to that.

Professor O'Leary from Dublin asked me searching questions about the way you canned and processed meat. What temperature did you have to cook it at to make it safe? My mind went blank. I hadn't got a clue.

As I was about to leave the exam room Professor

O'Leary rose from his chair, shook me by the hand and spoke.

'Young man, promise me this. No matter what you do in the veterinary profession, please don't make a career out of meat inspection. The public isn't ready for you.'

Wally's bar was in full swing. Half an hour to go and we'd know for sure. Time to drink, forget, and drink again.

It was Dave Bell who saw the list go up on the notice board outside the main lecture theatre. 'They're up,' he cried. 'Women and children first!'

I meant to walk over casual like. Honest I did. But you know how it is. Sometimes you just get caught up in the excitement of it all. I sprinted as fast as my legs would take me. So did everyone else.

And there it was: *Taylor, Nigel – Pass.*

I was on my way at last.

It's funny, the things you remember. There was a juke box playing full blast in Wally's bar. John Lennon sang 'Here comes the Sun' all afternoon. Someone said Betty Bright hadn't made it. Back for resits on Monday, they said. I couldn't be sure. I had to slip away to make a phone call.

'Hello mum, I hope you can hear me above the Beatles. I've done it, mum. I've bloody well gone and done it!'

36

There was a moment as the mighty engines of the 747 burst into life when I started to wonder if I was doing the right thing. It had all seemed so easy that night back in Princetown when Cameron Scott asked me what I was going to do once I left college. We'd been calving a really large South Devon cow. The calf was huge too and we'd had a real struggle. We sat exhausted on a couple of hay bales as we watched the newborn youngster tottering to his feet.

'I'm going to Canada,' I'd said enthusiastically. 'I've managed to get a job as an intern at the Ontario Veterinary College. I'm going to study and teach surgery.'

I was really excited about it all. North America seemed to be the place to go if you wanted to get on. Marvellous veterinary schools with wonderful facilities. You could learn a lot there. Why, in a few years you could even get to be a professor somewhere if you played your cards right and passed all your exams.

'You won't get in. Nobody ever does,' Betty Bright had told me when I let her know I was thinking of applying. 'They get applicants from all round the world. What makes you think you'll be accepted?'

'Someone's got to get it. It might as well be me,' I replied optimistically. I could see she wasn't convinced. One day a few weeks before finals the American and Canadian Veterinary Schools made their decisions. If you'd been selected you were telegrammed. You then had a day to accept or they offered it to someone else.

That weekend I'd had a job interview in Somerset. The vets there seemed pleasant enough and the practice was just the sort of enthusiastic place where I could be happy.

I never got there.

I was sitting in a lecture learning about nosebleeds in racehorses when the telegram arrived. The Ontario Veterinary College wanted me. All I had to do now was pass my finals.

That had been months ago. Since then I had worked as a locum in London and way up in the Highlands. I'd met a vet who wouldn't pay me and a pig I couldn't get pregnant. I'd begun to wonder what sort of life I'd let myself in for.

As the plane slowly climbed into the sky above south-east England that afternoon, it wasn't hard to see all the fields and farms laid out thousands of feet below. Down there vets were charging round, calving cows, treating puppies and doing the hundred and one other things that had made me want to become a veterinary surgeon in the first place. I was going to miss it. In a funny sort of way I felt I was letting the animals down by leaving them. But one day I'd be

247

back and I hoped that all the new skills I would learn would help me look after them even better.

High above England, lost in the cloud, the giant Air Canada jumbo altered course and headed out across the Atlantic. In a few hours I'd be in North America and a whole new veterinary world. There were great days ahead. I could hardly wait.